SCIENCE 3-6

Laying the foundations in the early years

Edited by Max de Bóo

Published by the Association for Science Education

Acknowledgements

Thanks to the following for supplying exemplar material and photographs:

Acresfield Nursery School, Middleton, Manchester (pp. 38, 48, 67)

Chater Infant School, Watford, Herts (cover, pp. 19, 23, 25, 33, 39, 57, 58, 66-73)

Kintore Way Nursery School, Lewisham (pp. 41, 44, 45)

Nursery staff of Kings Langley Primary School, Herts (p. 2)

Alison Bishop, Senior Lecturer, Primary Science, University of Northumbria

Gary Cornford (p. 77)

Lorna Ernst, BA(ECS) student, University of Hertfordshire (pp. 30, 63)

Helen Johnson (pp. 1, 26)

Peter Ovens (p. 17)

Wanda Parkes (p.75)

Others: authors' or editor's own.

Published by the Association for Science Education, College Lane, Hatfield, Hertfordshire AL10 9AA.
Tel: 01707 283000. Fax: 01707 266532. E-mail: ase@asehq.telme.com

Subediting: Helen Johnson

Design and page make-up: Colin Barker

Illustrations: Colin Barker and Ged Mitchell

Printed by Streets Printers, Royston Road, Baldock SG7 6NW

ISBN 0 86357 308 8

Contents

SCIENCE
3–6

Introduction			iv
Chapter 1	Why early-years science?	*Max de Bóo*	**1**
Chapter 2	Making sense of the national criteria	*Jane Johnston*	**7**
Chapter 3	Exploration and enquiry	*Sue Ellis and Sue Kleinberg*	**15**
Chapter 4	Children's language in science	*Rosemary Feasey*	**28**
Chapter 5	Science through everyday activities	*Pauline Boorman and Maggie Rogers*	**39**
Chapter 6	Assessment in the early years	*Brenda Keogh and Stuart Naylor*	**48**
Chapter 7	Promoting equality and citizenship	*John Siraj-Blatchford*	**57**
Chapter 8	Managing science in the early years	*Mary French and Audrey Randall*	**66**
Chapter 9	Planning the future	*Max de Bóo*	**75**
Appendix 1	Schemes of work for the early years		**80**
Appendix 2	Some basic resources for early-years enquiries		**87**
Appendix 3	Appropriate software resources		**89**
References			**90**

Introduction

There are numerous publications devoted to encouraging children's acquisition of language skills, numeracy, social and emotional skills but very few that discuss and exemplify young children's scientific development. The ASE (Association for Science Education) has not only the largest international subject membership in the world but includes early-years specialist educators among its membership. The Association is convinced of the value of good scientific teaching and learning in the early years and this book is the evidence of that belief. We need to show the way.

Although currently the birth-rate in Europe is falling, a combination of factors is resulting in the growth of playgroups, nurseries and reception classes:

● Many parents choose or need to be in full-time paid employment and want good child care in a stimulating learning environment.

● Families are smaller and young children with few or no siblings need opportunities to develop social and language skills away from home.

● Recent government initiatives suggest that there will be increased funding to support early childhood education.

We may need to redefine pre-school and early-childhood education – but whatever we do, we need to clarify and affirm what we believe to be good practice. This book attempts to do this and suggests ways of making it happen.

Chapter 1 looks at the *rationale* for science in the early years, particularly the chosen focus of 3–6 years. Early-years educators have been the Cinderellas of the teaching profession and, whilst none of the authors in this book would urge a subject-focused education for young children, it is important for teachers and carers of young children to know why science-based activities can provide children with generic, life-long skills. The acquisition of such skills is the first step to independent life-long learning.

Chapter 2 helps us to *make sense of national criteria*, criteria that are often statutory requirements. Jane Johnston leads us through recent developments in early-years science education and the need to break through the stereotypical view of scientists as male, lab-coated chemists. Jane goes on to set the scene for what we describe as 'good-quality learning' in science. The 4–5 year-old 'classroom chemists' give us a fascinating example of the nature of good-quality learning and how to recognise the science and encourage it.

Good practice includes learning through 'exploration and enquiry'. In **Chapter 3**, Sue Ellis and Sue Kleinberg explain how exploration and enquiry-based approaches can lead to good scientific learning. Enquiry-based approaches extend the children's thinking and knowledge. The authors clarify what an enquiry looks like and the positive outcomes of different types of enquiry. They show us how to see things from a young child's perspective, and remind us that young children can take over the responsibility for enquiry learning, given adult support and encouragement.

Chapter 4 looks at *language in science*. Rosemary Feasey describes how science is one of the best vehicles for stimulating children's speaking and listening, vocabulary and literacy, and how language can help scientific understanding.

Science is not constrained in the early years: it happens all over the place! In **Chapter 5**, Pauline Boorman and Maggie Rogers show how to recognise children's learning in science in *everyday activities* across the curriculum and how to encourage science in diverse activities such as designing and making or movement and dance.

Recognising and assessing young children's learning in science is necessary and can be a positive experience for both adults and children. In **Chapter 6**, Brenda Keogh and Stuart Naylor show how to *assess* young children's performance in science and enjoy doing it!

We have a diverse society. Science needs to identify with and value the richness of our children's different backgrounds and cultures. In **Chapter 7**, John Siraj-Blatchford discusses promoting *equality and citizenship*, defines some of the problems we need to tackle and offers some ideas for generating self-esteem in all our children.

Chapter 8 suggests how to plan for young children's scientific experience, pulling together much of what has been defined as good practice. Mary French and Audrey Randall give details of mid-term plans and how these can support good school policy, good practice in the classroom and good partnership with parents. These ideas are supported in **Appendix 1** by samples of material from local education authorities giving good advice for early-years science educators.

In **Chapter 9** Max de Bóo discusses the future possibilities and how to monitor the provision for early childhood education in science, to which end **Appendix 2** offers some ideas for appropriate science resources for 3–6 year-old children's scientific experiences.

Finally in **Appendix 3** we give a list of appropriate software resources.

Chapter 1

SCIENCE 3–6

Why early-years science?

Max de Bóo

> *The understanding of atomic physics is child's play compared with the understanding of child's play.*
>
> (David Kresch)

Why science?

Exploration and play

Science begins with children's very first acts of exploration: the baby looks around curiously and observes, reaches out to feel, puts things in her mouth to test and taste. Infancy is full of science: pulling things to see what happens, squeezing things with little fingers, banging fists on nearby objects. As the toddler acquires language, the questions begin: *'Why is the grass green?', 'Why is that dog doing a poo-poo?', 'Why can't I take my teeth out like Granddad does?'*

Exploring in the Science Museum

I *say* that this is science but in reality it is only the beginning of science. The child's exploration of the world is the springboard from which the next leap is taken, that of more systematic enquiry. Systematic enquiry may be described as 'science investigations' in later years (see Chapter 3). Nevertheless, the first step in any scientific enquiry is exploration, or 'play'.

The playful infant has no constraints on *time*. She will put the plastic rattle in her mouth

'It's all soft and slippy.'

again and again and again; the toddler will pour water time after time after time. At the end of such countless experiences the child 'knows' that the plastic rattle is hard against the gums, smooth against the tongue and makes a noise when it moves. The toddler 'knows' that water in the play tank is usually clear (i.e. transparent), that it 'pours', that it makes a 'splashy noise' when the surface is hit, that it 'wets' hands and clothes, and so on.

The 'system' being employed here is endless repetition which confirms that this rattle *always* does that, that *this* water always behaves like so. And in the middle of this we give children other non-plastic rattly things (a saucepan with dried peas inside) and water that isn't exactly the same as 'water' (ice cubes, orange juice, soapy, bubbly water). The children are not only having to absorb information about objects or phenomena in a streamlined, simple experiment, but have to infer the similarities and differences between them, or classify them, all at once. For example, the two rattles have a characteristic in common in that they both contain something that moves and hits against the material; the orange juice and soapy water both pour; the ice cubes melt into clear water and are *then* 'runny' like water.

We can sometimes underestimate the time needed by the infant to acquire skills and knowledge. But any scientist will confirm the length of time it takes to try out a new material, medicine or piece of technology. Tests are exhaustive before any claims can be made or a product put on to the market. Even so, it is easier for the scientist to test one new idea in laboratory conditions than for a child to test hundreds of new materials and phenomena simultaneously on a daily basis.

This is not to say we should impose limitations on early experiences – quite the contrary. We all seem to be born with the miraculous capacity to extract many of the relevant similarities from these experiences and begin the process of sorting our world into some sort of order. However, as the infant grows, there is more to learn and less time in which to learn it, less time for the countless repetitions of infancy, less time to make mistakes and correct them. Children need adult support to supply and simplify new experiences. Children need stimuli and scaffolding from adults to confirm or challenge the conclusions they are drawing from these new experiences (Bruner, Olver and Greenfield, 1966). In nurseries or early-years classrooms, time has to be structured so as to give children the maximum experience of familiar and unfamiliar phenomena in as short a time as possible, whilst still allowing enough repetitive play to convince them and enable them to make reasonable generalisations.

This 'scientific' approach to learning is endorsed by the Pre-school Playgroups Association (1991/2) who recommend that their playgroups should offer (amongst other things):

- safe stimulating environments for children to learn through exploration and experiment;
- access to equipment and activities that may not be available at home.

By the time children are 3 years old, their world includes abstract concepts like 'red-ness' or 'electricity' and

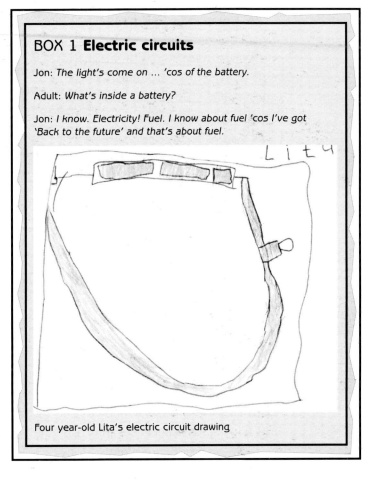

BOX 1 Electric circuits

Jon: *The light's come on ... 'cos of the battery.*

Adult: *What's inside a battery?*

Jon: *I know. Electricity! Fuel. I know about fuel 'cos I've got 'Back to the future' and that's about fuel.*

Four year-old Lita's electric circuit drawing

words and other symbols to read such as 'the', 'cat' and '2'. Exploration of the world moves into a phase where ideas can be articulated and represented in pictures and words (see Box 1 and Chapter 4).

Scientific enquiry

Science will still depend on curiosity and exploration, but increasingly involve asking questions, comparing and measuring, investigating or testing in a more structured way, drawing conclusions and making generalisations. Science is a process of acquiring knowledge by the application of these skills, over and over again. The argument for teaching science to young children is not that we should be introducing something *new* to them, it is simply that we continue the existing process of exploration and acquisition of knowledge about the world in a more efficient way (see Chapter 3).

If we are successful in helping children to be confident explorers, aware of their own scientific skills, how to apply them more consistently and economically (time-wise) and how to test their generalisations for possible flaws, we will have equipped them for life-long learning. Enquiry skills are generic and applicable in a variety of settings (see Chapter 2). Enquiry skills are also empowering: children become confident, independent learners (de Bóo, 1999). Faced with unfamiliar situations or new technology, such children know how to observe, compare, think and reason, generalise and apply their knowledge (see Chapter 5).

Knowledge

So far, I have been describing 'science' as an approach to learning – a set of attitudes (such as *curiosity*) and skills (such as *questioning* and *testing*). This emphasis has been deliberate. It is essential that young children's emerging skills are affirmed, reinforced and developed ('desirable outcomes' – DfEE, 1997). This is *the* priority – being scientific is a way of learning. However the word 'science' also denotes a body of knowledge. And indeed, there *is* a body of knowledge that we want our children to acquire: we want them to know that plants grow from seeds, that gravity pulls things down to the Earth, that the Moon reflects the light from the Sun. The problem with this is that, all too often, science is defined as *only* a body of knowledge, which can preclude or exclude the perception of science as a *method*, an approach to learning. Science is a way of life.

Why the early years?

In the early years, children are experiencing everything through their senses and through direct experience (Box 2). The body and the mind are inextricably linked – children need active practical learning in settings where they feel confident and valued (Johnston, 1996).

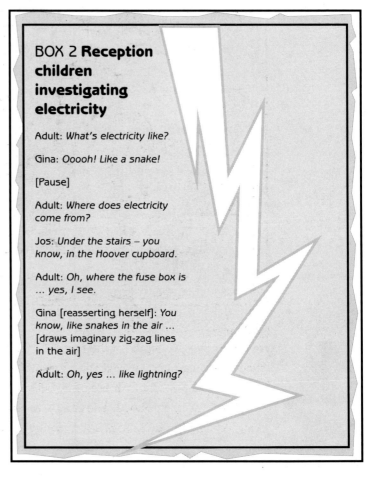

BOX 2 **Reception children investigating electricity**

Adult: *What's electricity like?*

Gina: *Ooooh! Like a snake!*

[Pause]

Adult: *Where does electricity come from?*

Jos: *Under the stairs – you know, in the Hoover cupboard.*

Adult: *Oh, where the fuse box is ... yes, I see.*

Gina [reasserting herself]: *You know, like snakes in the air ...* [draws imaginary zig-zag lines in the air]

Adult: *Oh, yes ... like lightning?*

Attitudes

Exploration or good play is only possible in stimulating but safe environments. Young children need more positive reassurance for their minor (and major) achievements – probably more than we give them at present – and less negative reinforcement. Success breeds success (Merry, 1998): good scientific behaviour in the future will depend on their positive attitude towards themselves and new situations. We need to make them constantly aware of how they are succeeding.

Often, we are in a hurry or surrounded by demanding children and can barely spare the time to 'tune in' to what at first sound like random or 'silly' utterances, such as Gina's in Box 2. When we can take time to listen and question, we often find that the children's comments are logically based on their previous experience. Sometimes children will use the evidence of their eyes together with their prior experience to make generalisations (hypotheses or 'theories') that are logical to them (see Box 3). Where possible, we can challenge their thinking without them losing self-esteem – in this example by introducing a new car.

Where challenges are not possible, we might respond by saying, '*It could be that. Shall we try it again?*' or '*I can see why you might think that.*' This affirms the child's thinking skills rather than focusing on any incorrect generalisation. Children are not fools – they hear the positive affirmation but also pick up the possible query and messages that 'it's OK to be mistaken sometimes' or 'there might be more than one answer'. All of this encourages open-mindedness – an attitude associated with science and an attitude we want all our children to develop.

Self-confidence and open-minded attitudes that have been encouraged in the early years, together with emerging scientific skills, help to establish a child's ability to learn in the future.

> **BOX 3 Robbie is rolling cars down a ramp to see which one goes the furthest.**
>
> Robbie: *The white one's gone furthest.*
>
> Adult: *Why's that, do you think?*
>
> Robbie: *'Cos it's a police car.*
>
> Adult: *Try this one. [a 'fast' non-police car]*
>
> [Robbie tries it – it goes further]
>
> Robbie: *Oh – it's not only police ones!*

When we look at a building, sturdy and beautiful, we only see the structure from ground level up. We do not see the depths of the foundations, the important services that enable the building to function, be warm and well-lit. This essential part of a building is hidden from view – but if the foundations are *not* there or are badly built, the building itself will crack or collapse. So it is with education in early childhood. The early years are not a 'holding period' until the *really important* education begins, *early-years education lays the foundations!*

Why 3–6 years?

Top-down education

Early childhood education has been the Cinderella in an education system that operates on a 'top-down' model. The average sum spent *per capita* on a sixth-form pupil (1998) is greater than that spent on a 5 year-old child, yet the resources needed for effective education of a 5 year-old are arguably equal to those required for a sixth-former. The salaries of teachers and carers reflect this emphasis too: the average salary of a secondary school teacher is higher than that of a primary teacher, yet the primary teacher has less non-contact time than the secondary teacher and has to deal with emotional as well as cognitive demands from the children. Nursery nurses and specialist teaching assistants are paid even less but fulfil essential roles in a young child's education. Staff and children in this age range need our support.

At the same time, there is increasing pressure placed on early-years educators to 'deliver the goods' for mainstream school. The advent of the National Curriculum for Science (1989 and onwards) meant that statutory requirements were laid down for children in key stage 1 (5–7 year-olds), particularly at the end of this stage, when their knowledge of science was tested (SATs) (see Chapter 2). The tests in science were subsequently dropped but the emphasis remained on the end of key stage 1 performance – in English and Mathematics. We now have a growing culture of 'teaching to the test'. In fact, in Western societies *'the mood everywhere around the child has become so serious'* (Tinbergen, 1976: 12).

The testing at the end of key stage 1 (and the end of key stage 2) meant that early-years educators felt pressurised to produce children who, regardless of their backgrounds or experience, could be measured by statutory criteria. It is certainly desirable to assess children's emerging skills and ideas for the benefit of parents and teachers, for diagnosis and planning (see Chapter 6), but not for the production of publicised league tables.

The Government subsequently published the document *Desirable outcomes for children's learning on entering compulsory education* (DfEE, 1997), which defined more general criteria for children's entitlement to learning about their world. The document had some serious flaws, for example the limited reference to our pluralist society (see Chapter 7), but did mention 'exploring our world' albeit in vague terms.

In reality, a young child's early development can be very different from that of a 7–8 year-old. The 3–6 year-old child is still largely learning through the medium of play or 'playful activities' (Moyles, 1989). It is inappropriate to start formal approaches too soon: *'Higher skills and knowledge are based on wide rather than restricted experiences'* (Moyles, 1989: 27) (see Chapter 5). Young children between the ages of 3 and 6 need to learn in an active non-sedentary environment which is synonymous with good practice. Making plans for this to happen is a demanding task but essential if we are to hang on to the playful approach to early-years learning (see Chapter 8).

The ultimate aim of education is to produce well-informed, scientifically literate citizens who can find things out for themselves, look critically at media or other information and make long-term decisions about their world, for themselves and the environment. The future is in their hands – the better we can educate our young children, the better that future will be.

Max de Bóo has spent many years working with young children, as a carer, a nursery teacher and in mainstream education, particularly at key stage 1. She has worked as an advisory teacher for science, supporting educators from early years to year 6. Max is currently a senior lecturer in education at the University of Hertfordshire, specialising in science and early-years education. She has written widely on these subjects and acts as a consultant and in-service training provider at a national level. Her interests and research have focused on young children's scientific thinking, language and science, and student-teachers' scientific background.

Chapter 2

SCIENCE
3–6

Making sense of the national criteria

Jane Johnston

> **Adult: What is a scientist?**
>
> **Child: Is it a man who has something to do with chemicals and things?**

Children's entitlement to science education

Primary science and early-years education have been areas of increasing interest in recent years. One of the outcomes of this interest was the legislation to ensure that all children, from pre-school to 16 years of age, have some consistency in education and access to scientific experiences. National Curriculum documents for England and Wales (DFE 1995), Scotland (SOED, 1993), and Northern Ireland (NIED, 1995) have defined the science education that children are entitled to receive.

However, the constant changes to national criteria, the tinkering with the curriculum and the lack of support for teachers has left us with a very confusing picture of what constitutes good early-years education. The prevailing view of science is still of white-coated men who have *'something to do with chemicals and things'*, who are on the fringes of 'normal' human society and deal with abstract irrelevant facts. Our curriculum partly reflects this view by placing little value on affective (emotional, personal, attitudinal) development and providing poor support for developing process skills or even the actual interpretation of the documentation.

As a result, the period of rapid change is not yet complete. We need to consider ways of clarifying documentation and providing support for early-years educators. We want young children to experience the awe and wonder of the world around them and develop the conceptual understanding, skills and attitudes important for future life.

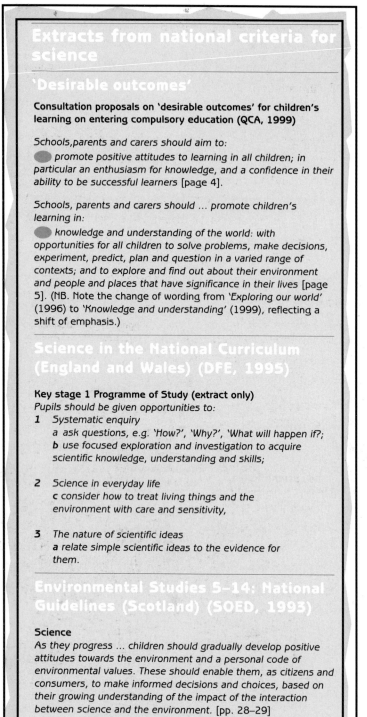

Extracts from national criteria for science

'Desirable outcomes'

Consultation proposals on 'desirable outcomes' for children's learning on entering compulsory education (QCA, 1999)

Schools, parents and carers should aim to:
● *promote positive attitudes to learning in all children; in particular an enthusiasm for knowledge, and a confidence in their ability to be successful learners* [page 4].

Schools, parents and carers should ... promote children's learning in:
● *knowledge and understanding of the world: with opportunities for all children to solve problems, make decisions, experiment, predict, plan and question in a varied range of contexts; and to explore and find out about their environment and people and places that have significance in their lives* [page 5]. (NB. Note the change of wording from 'Exploring our world' (1996) to 'Knowledge and understanding' (1999), reflecting a shift of emphasis.)

Science in the National Curriculum (England and Wales) (DFE, 1995)

Key stage 1 Programme of Study (extract only)
Pupils should be given opportunities to:
1 Systematic enquiry
    a ask questions, e.g. 'How?', 'Why?', 'What will happen if?;
    b use focused exploration and investigation to acquire scientific knowledge, understanding and skills;

2 Science in everyday life
    c consider how to treat living things and the environment with care and sensitivity,

3 The nature of scientific ideas
    a relate simple scientific ideas to the evidence for them.

Environmental Studies 5–14: National Guidelines (Scotland) (SOED, 1993)

Science
As they progress ... children should gradually develop positive attitudes towards the environment and a personal code of environmental values. These should enable them, as citizens and consumers, to make informed decisions and choices, based on their growing understanding of the impact of the interaction between science and the environment. [pp. 28–29]

The development of national criteria

While the pace of change in primary science has traditionally been rather slow, since the 1980s it has been fairly dramatic, with pre-school science following a little more sedately behind. In the early 1980s, primary science focused mainly on the development of 'process' or scientific skills. Change was generally on the periphery of mainstream education and developments were localised, despite efforts to improve provision through national projects (e.g. Schools Council *Science 5/13* project, 1967–74).

The Education Reform Act (DES, 1989) identified science as a core subject, an essential part of the primary school curriculum, alongside mathematics and English. The early reports on science in the primary curriculum (DES/WO, 1987) recognised the balance and interrelationship between conceptual understanding, process skills and attitudes, although assessment emphasised knowledge and understanding. Unfortunately, subsequent documentation (DES/WO, 1989, 1991; DFE, 1995) gave less and less importance to scientific attitudes and the nature and history of science.

The changing criteria within the documentation may reflect our developing beliefs and values about what constitutes science, good education and the nature of early-years science. Our beliefs and values are bound to be affected by our society, culture and the political situation which are also in a state of continual change. The present national criteria for pre-school (DfEE, 1997), key stage 1 (DFE, 1995) and P1–P3 (SOED, 1993) specify the essential ingredients in the science curriculum. However, they send very mixed and incomplete messages about the nature of early-years science education. Such a rapid and piecemeal approach to educational development will probably always result in omissions and misinterpretations, and the desire to keep documentation manageable results in a lack of supportive guidelines.

Knowledge and understanding

Conceptual understanding appears to be the main focus of documentation because national criteria favour knowledge and understanding as an indicator of achievement. Even this creates difficulties because our criteria and the assessment process actually focus on knowledge rather than understanding (*'I can tell you the answer but I don't know what it means'* – see Chapter 6). Improvements in the 1995 edition of the science criteria (see panel) led to clearer interpretation of what is appropriate for young children but the pre-school criteria are vague and unhelpful and open to misinterpretation. Exemplification material (SCAA, 1997) gave limited help in identifying scientific development in key stage 1.

What is clear is that we need to reflect now on what is good early-years science education and what is missing from present documentation.

What do the national criteria leave out?

On the one hand, messages about the practical nature of science have been strong, emphasising the importance of the process skills (Sc1 in the National Curriculum, DFE, 1995) and giving them equal status with conceptual understanding (Sc2–4).

On the other hand, omitting the word 'exploration' from the title in Sc1 (changed in 1995) leads us to believe that science should be experimental or investigative, neither of which is wholly appropriate to early years. For young children, science enquiries should be exploratory, encouraging children to observe, raise questions about their observations, group similar objects, interpret their observations and communicate their ideas to others. These explorations will often lead to more systematic investigations but many early-years experiences are not, and should not be, investigative.

The National Curriculum gives no support to teachers as to how to identify and develop the children's skills (some support can be found in local authority and commercial schemes – see Appendix 1). The proposed new 'Early learning goals' (DfEE, 1999) are also unclear on how to implement the requirements. However, skills still feature as important, skills such as *'asking questions, finding out, observing, and talking about ...'.* This is a better model for children's exploration of their world.

Figure 1 **Elements of science (after Ratcliffe, 1998)**

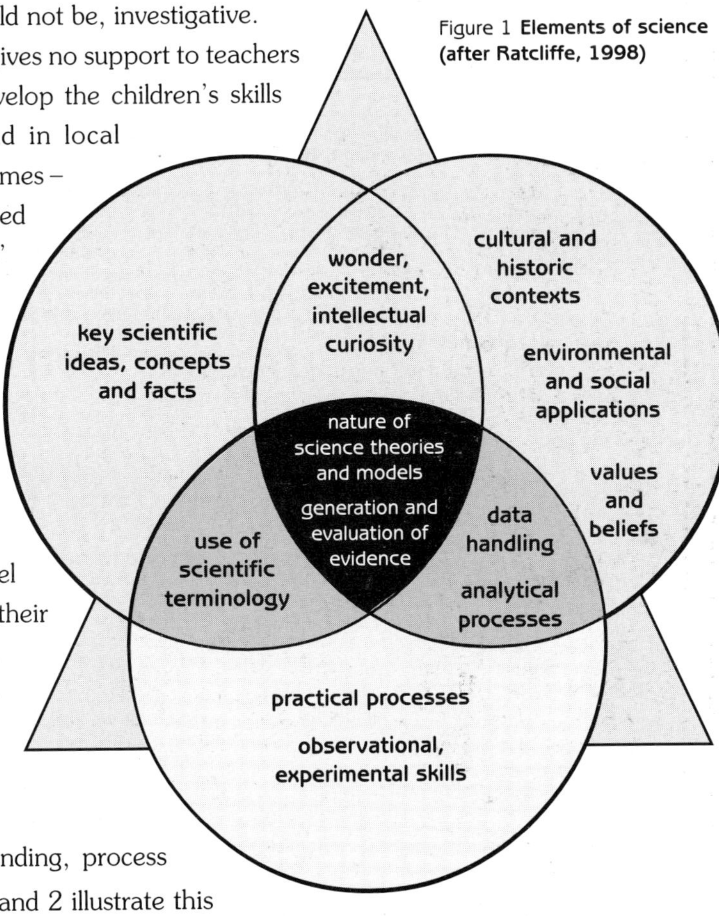

key scientific ideas, concepts and facts

wonder, excitement, intellectual curiosity

cultural and historic contexts

environmental and social applications

nature of science theories and models

generation and evaluation of evidence

use of scientific terminology

data handling

values and beliefs

analytical processes

practical processes

observational, experimental skills

Good quality learning in science

Learning in science is a complex interrelationship between conceptual understanding, process skills and attitudes. Figures 1 and 2 illustrate this interrelationship in two different ways. The interaction of the different dimensions is essential in young children's learning and formal schooling, and everyday experiences link the relevant contexts for continuous learning.

The complex nature of young children's learning can make it difficult to identify the science and reference it accurately to national documents. Nevertheless, with practice, it is possible to clarify the aims of activities and be confident that children are acquiring knowledge and skills and developing appropriate attitudes. We can define our aims as **focus**, **interaction** and **context**, that is, the learning purpose, the way in which the adult might intervene, and the activity that will encourage learning.

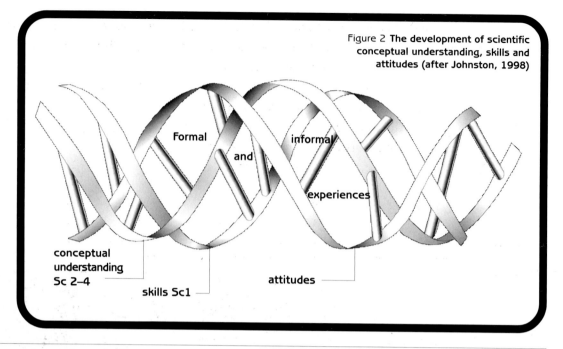

Figure 2 **The development of scientific conceptual understanding, skills and attitudes (after Johnston, 1998)**

The focus, or learning purpose

Science-based activities will encompass all aspects of learning. The case studies (Boxes 1 and 2) illustrate how we can identify and reference the focuses or learning purposes in science and other learning. In the first case, Box 1, the aims of the activity were to develop:

- enthusiasm, speculation and decision-making (attitudes);
- understanding of the relevance and the history of science (attitudes);
- observational and classification skills (skills);
- knowledge and understanding of medical, historical artefacts and early technology (concepts).

[Desirable outcomes (DfEE, 1997): Exploring our world; Personal, social and emotional development (PSE). National Curriculum for Science (DFE, 1995): PoS and Sc1 (skills), Sc2 (ourselves). Scottish Curriculum (SOED, 1993): P1–P3 Environmental Studies – Science]

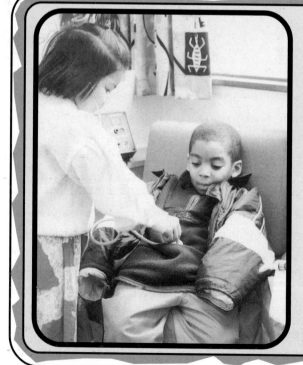

BOX 1 A medical enquiry

Young children (aged 4–5) were given a range of medical artefacts such as: liquorice sticks (obtained from a health food shop), dock leaves, a stethoscope, clean empty boxes which once contained patent medicines, plasters, a clean empty inhaler, an ear trumpet (for listening to the heart), a bandage and some maggots in a jar.

The adults encouraged the children to observe the artefacts, identify what they were and how they might be used, which ones today and which ones in the past.

The children explored the objects and sorted them, and some were selected for the play area, now set up as a doctor's surgery.

Following up the activity in Box 1, the children were asked to design a new medicine by mixing a selection of liquids and solids (Johnston and Gray, 1999), with safe monitoring (Box 2). In this case, the learning objectives were:

● understanding of materials and their properties and that some materials change when they are mixed together (conceptual development);

● observing, predicting, testing and reasoning (developing skills);

● practical experience of capacity (mathematics);

● physical and creative development;

(etc.)

[Desirable outcomes (DfEE, 1997): Exploring our world, Maths, etc. National Curriculum (DFE, 1995): Sc1, Sc3, Maths. Scottish Curriculum (SOED, 1993): P1–P3, Environmental Studies – Science & Maths]

BOX 2 Making a new medicine

Materials were selected that give interesting effects when mixed together. Those given to the children included six solids:

bicarbonate of soda, sugar, salt, talcum powder, plaster of Paris, cornflour

and six liquids:

vegetable oil, *Matey Wizard* bubble bath, white vinegar, washing-up liquid, lemon juice, water.

All substances were in identical containers with numbers or letters identifying them (although coloured stickers could be used). The children were asked to predict what would happen if small amounts of each of the different substances were mixed with water.

Each child tried out her or his chosen mixture to see what happened. Some bubbled, some fizzed, some separated and sank, some dissolved. They repeated this with two different substances (two liquids or a liquid and a solid).

Joseph exclaimed, '*Mine has gone blue!*' [Matey bubble bath changes colour with temperature, acidity (lemon juice and vinegar) and alkalinity (bicarbonate of soda and washing-up liquid).

Sarah said, '*Mine's fizzing!*' [she had mixed bicarbonate of soda and vinegar which releases bubbles of carbon dioxide in the chemical reaction].

Ayse said, '*Mine's hot!*' [mixing water with plaster of Paris gives out heat in an exothermic reaction].

The children discovered that oil and water don't mix (water is denser than oil), sugar and salt dissolve in water, talcum powder clumps in water and cornflour forms a sort of liquidy-solid that runs through your fingers unless you squeeze it, when it appears more solid.

Subsequent activities focused on further exploration of the materials, mixing their own medicines (taking care not to mishandle or taste any materials), and deciding what their medicine would be good for. Older children in the group designed an advert to sell their medicine and looked at advertisements for other medicines in magazines and from the past (creative development and technology). The children showed excitement, cooperation and perseverance (desirable outcomes: PSE). This was followed up by stories of great medical scientists and doctors from the past (language and literacy) (Johnston and Gray, 1999). Learning about science is an important aspect of scientific development. We often forget the scientists, men and women, who have made our lives healthier by their research and determination.

> Clare Lare Levy
> I think that a scienristis
> Some – one who dose a Lot
> of work like drawing
> and writeing and telling
> pepole About Long ago.
>
> ---
>
> Alexandra Jane Smith
> I Think that a Scienrist
> is Some – one who wers thos
> funny Shors in hot countrys.
> and they do pictures for
> billdings.

Adult intervention

The case studies illustrate how exploring the materials motivated the children to learn. Furthermore, the adults' questions and challenges inspired and enriched the children's experiences.

Adult intervention throughout is a vital ingredient. Teachers, classroom assistants, nursery nurses and parents all act as role models for the developing child. Adults who are uninterested or less than enthusiastic about the world around them, who show no curiosity or interest in things, will send negative messages about science. Conversely, adults who are enthusiastic, questioning, value new experiences and have an obvious love for learning will provide positive role models for children.

Adults involved in supporting the developing child should work together in partnership (see Chapter 8), interacting with children during experiences, encouraging them and motivating them. They will ask questions that focus on the learning objectives and provide challenges to develop new ideas, skills and attitudes.

Helping children to develop their science skills

We cannot develop all skills at all times. We need to be able to identify specific scientific skills and know how these develop. For example, the skill of **interpretation** is often neglected in a busy classroom but, without requests to **reflect** on their experiences and interpret these, children will not consolidate or modify their ideas. **Communicating** is an essential skill in science as in all learning. Children need opportunities to think and clarify their ideas and explain them to others. This often helps them to evaluate their ideas.

Reflecting, interpreting and communicating can be developed by:

- allowing time at the end of science experiences for this process;
- encouraging children to share their findings;
- discussing interpretations with the children;

● making use of circle time;

● asking children to pose new questions, for themselves or others, in a new exploration;

● questioning children about their experiences;

● encouraging children to identify what they have learned.

Obviously, this kind of detailed support is not always possible, and it is not written in the documentation, but without it children may be 'doing activities' without knowing 'why'.

Helping children to develop positive attitudes

As stated earlier, changing documentation has decreased the emphasis on scientific attitudes, both attitudes *in* science (curiosity, sensitivity to living things, etc.) and attitudes *to* science – the attitudes that determine the way we view science and its relevance to our lives and society (see page 8). Figure 3 shows how scientific attitudes are linked to process skills.

Figure 3 **The process of developing scientific attitudes**

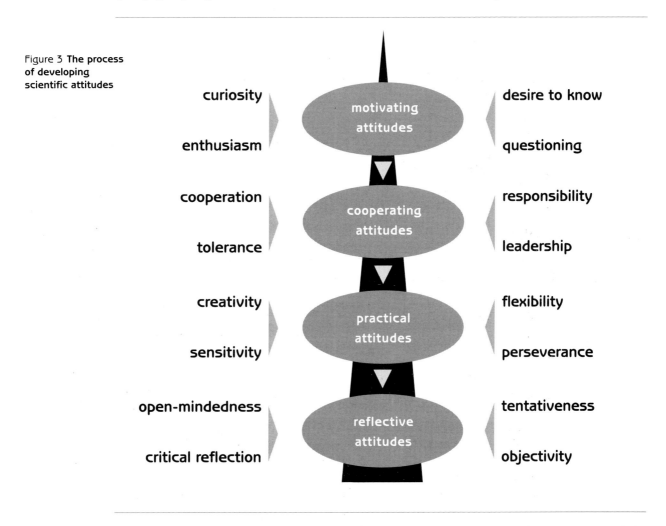

These attitudes can easily be developed alongside process skills and conceptual understanding as shown in Figure 2. It is important that we enthuse children with the wonders of science, make them curious about the world around them and motivate them to want to find out more about scientific phenomena. We need to:

● provide children with safe but stimulating experiences;

● help them work cooperatively with others (science involves teamwork);

● show children that we are flexible and value the world around us (attitudes are contagious!);

● show open-mindedness ourselves so as to encourage children's reflective attitudes, such as being objective and tentative about jumping to conclusions.

The context of learning

The context of learning is an important part of the learning process because it is through an appropriate context that children are motivated, challenged and then progress. Experiences that are set in an irrelevant context, utilising abstract ideas unrelated to children's everyday lives, are less successful than experiences that are relevant, practical and illustrate the holistic, cross-curricular nature of science (see Chapter 5).

Current national criteria that define early–years science education (DfEE, 1997 and DFE, 1995) do not provide us with ideas and support to develop attitudes and the learning environment and, worse still, appear to emphasise the stereotypical view of a scientist as *'a man who has something to do with chemicals and things'* (Johnston, 1992).

We want our children to feel enthusiastic and curious about the world around them. We need to motivate them with stimulating experiences and encourage systematic, practical skills to enable them to succeed in tasks and solve problems. We need to encourage cooperative attitudes (so that valuable time is not wasted on minor disputes), sensitivity towards their world and flexibility in their approach. Finally, to develop conceptually from their experiences, children need to have certain reflective attitudes, such as objectivity and tentativeness.

We can help children achieve this. The case studies illustrate how the provision of stimulating materials and safe opportunities to explore the materials motivated the children to become scientists themselves, to investigate, solve problems and go on to apply their skills and knowledge in a new but familiar situation.

However, we need good national guidelines with appropriate criteria and approaches for the early years if we are to help children develop into confident, scientifically literate citizens of tomorrow.

Jane Johnston has considerable experience of primary teaching, including responsibilities for science and special educational needs. She is now a senior lecturer in primary education at Bishop Grosseteste College, where she specialises in early years and primary science education. Her particular interests are in early-years science education and the development of attitudes to science and she has gained national funding for developing the public understanding of science, both in the UK and Australia. Jane is an established author and consultant in these areas.

Chapter 3

SCIENCE 3–6

Exploration and enquiry

Sue Ellis and Sue Kleinberg

Chris and Phil, aged 5, are trying to make a bed for the doll in the home-corner but the doll is too heavy. They keep rearranging the yoghurt pot bed legs until the weight distribution is satisfactory.

Young children aged about 3–6 and in educational settings need to learn *through* enquiry and they need to learn *to* enquire. They need to do this not only to fulfil the demands of the science curriculum but also to become citizens who are interested in the world around them and feel that they have an active part to play in finding out about our world and influencing its future development.

Children need to be engaged with exploration, investigations, and enquiry if they are, over time, to build up ideas of:

- why science is done;
- what doing science involves;
- science as something they can and want to do themselves.

It is important to develop these ideas, skills and attitudes in young children because it helps them to see a purpose in, and make sense of, their later and more formal lessons in science. An emphasis on enquiry-based learning within the science curriculum provides a sound basis for learning. It can help to ensure that children understand that:

- science is about understanding the real world and not just about special classroom activities initiated by adults;
- science knowledge is about our immediate environment, accessible and interesting;
- we need to work from real evidence, not just from what we think or would like to think;
- finding out about something and understanding it takes time, thought and careful observation.

Enquiry-based learning helps us to ensure that young children become interested in and knowledgeable about their world. Their scientific understanding becomes firmly rooted in everyday activities and experiences, providing a basis for generalisations and discussions in more de-contextualised ways.

Understanding the young child's perspective

To introduce children to the different purposes of enquiry and lead them to investigate, we need to recognise their starting points in terms of their development, competence and achievements.

Young children are:

- curious;
- immediate;
- interested in their immediate environment;
- imaginative and empathetic;
- theorisers and sense makers;
- collaborators and educators.

Anyone who has watched a toddler repeatedly flushing the toilet or pulling the magnetic tape out of a cassette knows that young children are born enquirers. They fiddle and play with things to see what happens.

However, whilst we have come to see young children as more competent and skilled theorisers than was once the case (see, for example, Desforges, 1993; Bruner, 1996), the meaning they take from situations is necessarily limited by their lack of experience and knowledge. Few 5 year-olds connect the effects of boiling rice, potatoes and pasta and see the commonality between them, let alone understand the underpinning scientific principle. Few 3 year-olds can measure with standard units or see the reason to do so. Young children frequently use story-telling to explain cause and effect or animal behaviour and it is important that they are allowed to do this. They ascribe attributes to non-human animals on the grounds of similarity to themselves (Carey, 1985) and, as Millar *et al.* (1995) have shown, it is rare for 9 year-olds to use even a simple scientific framework for their investigations.

But young children do seek connections, as Box 1 shows. Chris, aged 6, may not be correct but shows a real quest to understand – and maybe some inkling of the turbine?

Often, sheer lack of knowledge or experience of the world means that the focus of a young child's interest

---

BOX 1 **The Romans**

Year 1 were doing a topic on the Romans and had been discussing the layout of the Roman villa. One feature they noted was the pond in the courtyard. The next day they were told that Roman villas had heated floors. Chris seemed to think for a while and then stated, 'So they must have had electricity!' The teacher asked, 'What makes you think that?' 'Because the pond goes down ... and ... the water goes round, round a big machine to the heating.'

or questions is different. The children make glitter shakers. When the shaker is turned, some sequins go down; other shapes cut from shiny wrapping materials float and rise up. To 3 or 4 year-olds this is not remarkable because they have not had enough experience of floating and sinking to expect things that look similar to act in a similar way. However, 6 year-olds are fascinated about why it happens. Similarly, the fact that an orange sinks when it is peeled, but floats with the peel on, is just accepted by younger children, whereas older ones question it because they have had more experience of the world.

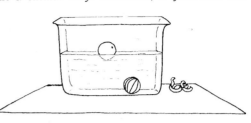

Young children need plenty of time to explore and undertake hands-on enquiries with time to go up blind alleys. Three year-olds working with Lego will learn largely through trial and error and imitation; 6 year-olds can identify problems in their construction and learn from discussion and explanations. Time for exploration is important not only to become familiar with materials and tools but for questions to arise and be pursued. These experiences help develop strategies, skills and knowledge which can be seen as emergent science.

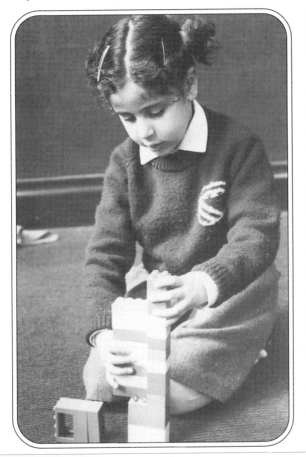

'It's going to be a big tower.'

This highlights the need for educators concerned with science to have a sound knowledge of the nature of young children and the importance of early learning. Working with a knowledge of the nature of young children and the value of their early experiences is increasingly important (see Pollard, 1997) when we are becoming aware of the detrimental effects of too early an introduction to formal education. If, for example, young children are rushed into the mechanics of reading or arithmetic they may well acquire the skills but, unless they understand the basic cultural rules of what number and reading are used for, who uses them and how, then *'their lack of sense of a wider purpose will always hinder spontaneous learning'* (Munn and Kleinberg, 1998).

What is an enquiry?

Exploration can be satisfying in its own right but can also initiate an enquiry. An enquiry can be conceptualised as having three phases:

● getting started;
● keeping going;
● looking back.

Getting started involves framing a question and then forming a plan. In a topic on forces/friction the question may be about shoes, such as, 'Which soles grip best?' Forming a plan can involve an examination of the different shoes the children wear and the choice of a surface on which to test them.

Keeping going involves the children in putting the plan into action and testing the slipperiness of the soles, being persistent and consistent, making an assessment of how things are going,

then deciding to stop because they have enough information to answer their question.
Looking back involves interpreting the results (in this case deciding that rubber soles are less likely to slip than leather ones) and explaining the results ('rubber is a stickier material': ideas of friction). Looking back also involves evaluating the plan (Did we test enough different soles? Was the test fair? Did we do the same – or use the same person – in each test?).

Uses and types of enquiry

In teaching science to children, enquiries are used for different purposes and take many forms. All have played important parts in the lives of real scientists and can be part of the early stages of science.

Enquiries may be used to:

● generate interest;

● make teaching points;

● develop skills.

They may be:

● practical/empirical enquiries;

● book-based enquiries;

● thought/talk-based enquiries.

Using enquiry to generate interest

Sometimes enquiry is used simply to generate intellectual interest and provide common experiences (e.g. observation). For example, children observe 'snow' scene shakers at Christmas and note that the snowflakes don't all fall straight down. Older children are interested in why. They note that it also happens in real life when snowflakes fall through the air (younger ones just accept this). The enquiry can be aided through a range of physical activities (see Chapter 5) such as drama/dance: behaving like a snowflake and behaving like rain before seeking to explain the difference between snow and rain falling. Such an enquiry generates the interest, experiences, observations and social negotiation on to which the explanation can be grafted.

Using enquiry to make teaching points

Sometimes an enquiry arises from a teaching point. An adult in a nursery class tells the children that leaves have different shapes. The children begin to make a collection of leaves. The adult asks the children to think of ways to describe the differences between the leaves – the start of learning about scientific classification.

Using enquiry to develop skills

Sometimes the purpose of an enquiry is the acquisition or consolidation of a skill. Table-top magnifying glasses, set up beside growing plants, encourage children to explore the effect of distance and angle on what and how they see.

Practical/empirical enquiries

Children dropping balls made of plastic, rubber and fabric on to a hard wooden surface stop to listen and then compare the different sounds they make.

Book-based enquiries

Some children very interested in frogs have a good collection of books about them. They look through all their books to find out how many different types of frogs there are and how they differ from each other. Another group are interested in finding out about the life-cycle stories of different animals. Science can provide a purposeful stimulus to literacy.

Thought/talk-based enquiries

Children are discussing amongst themselves the different heights of the platforms that they have been jumping from, and what it felt like. They take the discussion point to its logical end: *'What do you think would happen if you jumped from something a bit higher, like a box? A lot higher like a table? Even higher than that, like the climbing frame? or a house?'* – *'That would definitely kill you,'* says one child.

Can free play be an enquiry?

Free play often poses challenges for adults. How do we decide whether the play is enquiring and relevant to science? When young children engage in their own free enquiries, the brevity, opportunism and amount of extraneous, creative *'storying'* that goes on often looks highly unscientific (see Box 2).

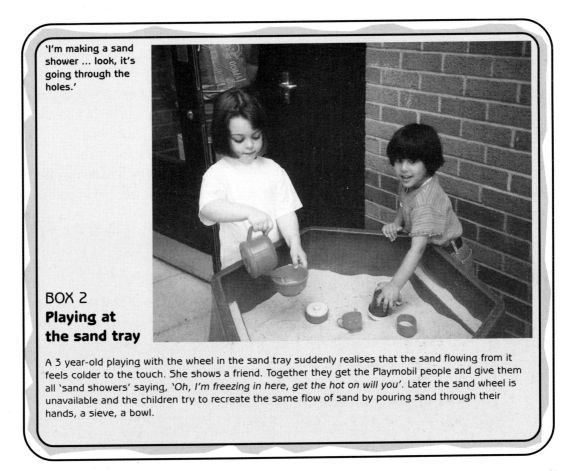

'I'm making a sand shower ... look, it's going through the holes.'

BOX 2
Playing at the sand tray

A 3 year-old playing with the wheel in the sand tray suddenly realises that the sand flowing from it feels colder to the touch. She shows a friend. Together they get the Playmobil people and give them all 'sand showers' saying, 'Oh, I'm freezing in here, get the hot on will you'. Later the sand wheel is unavailable and the children try to recreate the same flow of sand by pouring sand through their hands, a sieve, a bowl.

In terms of the three phases of the enquiry model outlined, it is sometimes difficult to know whether the children are working at an enquiry or exploring. Free play can lead to or be nudged towards an enquiry, but it often lacks the structure of an enquiry in that the questions and challenges arise as things happen, rather than according to a plan. Like Topsy it just grows! This is, we suggest, a stage in the development of children's capacity to engage in enquiry – and a very important one for young children. They are action-orientated and respond to immediate events; over time they become more conscious of their learning, how they learn and the idea of a plan.

BOX 3 Children's questions about bees (de Boo, 1985)

Karis: *Why are bees smaller than butterflies?*

Ayse: *Why do bees have six legs?*

Peter: *How did the first bee come alive?*

Samantha: *Why do bees have lines on their wings like leaves?*

Thomas: *Why do they sting?*

Damian: *Why don't we have any King bees?*

Enquiry skills

Learning *to* enquire

Children need to be helped to learn skills and strategies that will help them to enquire. They need to be able to observe, to question, to predict, test, and so on. Such skills and strategies, concepts and constructs are not specific to science in the early years but are generic skills. It will take many years of guided and discussed experiences before they approximate to the ideas and skills of the adult world and are refined to take on the characteristic features related to specific disciplines. A question is a question to a young child and what constitutes a good question in science as opposed to a good question in art takes a long time to learn (see Box 3). Learning to enquire requires habits and dispositions such as patience, attending to events, remembering, taking care and caring.

Learning *through* enquiry

Young children need to engage in *authentic* enquiries (appropriate and relevant to them) if they are to use and develop their skills and strategies and to see them as useful, powerful and worthwhile tools which lead to knowledge. Learning to like 'learning through enquiry' and value it as a way of working requires that children have a vested interest in the enquiry. They need respect for their questions, issues which interest them and some degree of control over the enquiry process.

Whose enquiry is it?

If children are to learn to enquire and learn through enquiring then they need experience of being involved in the decision-making. Who makes decisions about the three phases of *getting started*, *keeping going* and *looking back*?

Adult control

Faced with the desire to 'do science' with young children, adults often end up shunting the

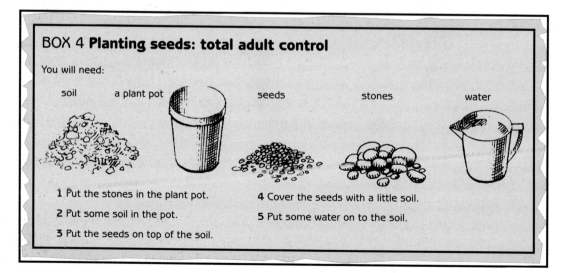

BOX 4 Planting seeds: total adult control

You will need:

soil   a plant pot   seeds   stones   water

1 Put the stones in the plant pot.

2 Put some soil in the pot.

3 Put the seeds on top of the soil.

4 Cover the seeds with a little soil.

5 Put some water on to the soil.

child through a series of pre-ordained steps. The child carries out instructions but has little say either in what is being investigated or how. In this situation the adult decides and controls everything: the question, the plan, the keeping going and the evaluation. All phases are decreed by the adult. A typical example is that of planting seeds and using an instruction sheet (Box 4).

With total control, the adult at best can be said to be modelling a process for the child. However, the children are actively engaged and interested because of the adult's skills in involving and 'translating' the adult decisions being made. Clearly, this sort of experience is important for children. However, if this adult-controlled event is the *only* experience children have of enquiry, it is likely that they will grow up to view enquiry as:

● something that can only happen when an adult is present to tell them what to do;

● something initiated and controlled by the adult.

Shared control

Allowing and encouraging children to take decisions is motivating to them and strengthens their strategies, skills and knowledge. Parents, teachers, classroom assistants, indeed anyone working alongside young children, need to encourage children to take part in making decisions. Imagine 'planting seeds' done in different ways and the rich learning outcomes that might occur (Box 5).

BOX 5 **Planting seeds: joint enquiries**

• Collect seeds from outside. Where do we find them? How do they get separated from the plant? Do all plants have seeds?

• Look through and sort a variety of seeds before choosing which one to plant. Will a big seed grow into a big plant? Will they all grow equally well? Will they all take the same amount of time to germinate?

• Children plant their seeds. What happens when a seed germinates? Children draw the various stages of growth. Do all seedlings grow in the same way? Children compare their own seedlings with others of the same type, and with different types. They look in books to find more examples.

'My radishes are the biggest!'

Child control

The other end of the continuum to total adult control is an enquiry in which all decisions are made by the child or children. They generate the question or task to be tackled, plan how to 'answer' the question, execute their plan, and judge the adequacy of their solution and approach. Free-play situations can be seen as a forum for such enquiry. They can give rise to

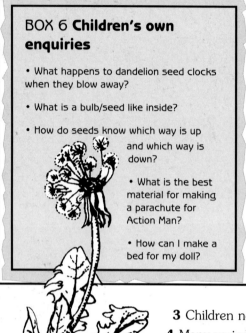

BOX 6 Children's own enquiries

- What happens to dandelion seed clocks when they blow away?

- What is a bulb/seed like inside?

- How do seeds know which way is up and which way is down?

- What is the best material for making a parachute for Action Man?

- How can I make a bed for my doll?

the need to know and work things out, provide the time to work through things at the child's pace and alongside interested friends. In these contexts, we see children asking their own questions (Box 6).

The context for good enquiry learning

The following seven principles derived from the above provide a good context for developing enquiry learning:

1 Enquiries should be set in real-life contexts relevant to the children, i.e. 'situated' or everyday science.

2 Topics or centres of interest should be used to stimulate enquiries.

3 Children need to be allowed time to pursue enquiries.

4 Many varied and *repeated* experiences should be provided.

5 Children need encouragement to learn *to* enquire and learn *through* enquiry.

6 An informed adult can support and challenge children's ideas.

7 The context needs to be open-ended, celebratory and enthusiastic.

Real-life contexts

Children need 'situated' or everyday science in which the ideas and enquiries are presented, not in terms of abstract adult 'scientific' knowledge and activities, but in terms of the everyday experiences of the young child, relevant to them and their environment.

Adults' provision of early experience should be informed by scientific frameworks but operate with a broader model than the classroom or laboratory model that children will meet later. If young children always see science as being something that arises out of adult-initiated activities or resources (i.e. as what you do when the science table or box is out), they will not believe in its power to help them understand and investigate their world. They will be on the path to learning 'classroom science', divorced from real concerns or real experiences, like older children who learn about evaporation and condensation but see no connection between these ideas and what happens to the bathroom mirror when they have a hot bath.

Topics/centres of interest

The use of topics or centres of interest is a powerful stimulus. For example, water can be the meaningful route to ideas about floating, reflection, dissolving and the associated concepts and constructs of forces, light and properties of materials. With younger children this seems a powerful way of learning science, recognising that there is so much generic, holistic learning to be accomplished.

A lengthy topic is not always necessary. Many explorations can arise in a serendipitous manner if the adult creates a context for them. The inclusion of intriguing objects such as mirrors, torches or coloured acetates on the interest table can give rise to exploratory play which may well be nudged by the adult towards a more developed enquiry. With older infants who have some experience, posing questions can function as an impetus to enquiry. Similarly, visits to a building site, nature walks, use of the climbing frame, cooking and kaleidoscopes can all provide the impetus to observe and question what is happening and why.

'This one will float on top.'

Time

Children do need time to pursue their own enquiries. Young children need time and encouragement to explore. Storying (see pages 54–55) is often important – it keeps children on task and interested. Storying and play allow thinking time and encourage children to spend time 'fiddling about' and 'thinking things through', both of which are an important part of observation. They build up their hands-on experience and knowledge so that they have a base from which to ask questions and link to existing knowledge.

Varied and repeated experiences

In order to have a good base from which to enquire, young children need many varied and repeated experiences. It is not sufficient to plant bulbs just once with an adult. A child may need to plant many different types of bulbs many times – sometimes with an adult, sometimes alone, sometimes with other children. By observing what they do alone and what they talk about with others, the adult will gauge their understanding and also allow the children the thinking time to make connections with other experiences and do the sort of unpressured 'wondering' that leads them to generate their own questions. The children may need to revisit bulbs they have planted, digging them up to see what is happening, as well as growing seeds and plants in different ways, so that they get a sense of what is central to the process of growth.

'My seeds are growing!

Children need the experience and knowledge presented to them through activities in which they are engaged, and vicariously through stories of what other children do in books, descriptions of what they and others have done at home, picture sequences so that they can remember and reflect on what they have done in the nursery/school and information texts that describe the process. Only when they get this foundation and support will recognisably 'scientific' questions arise.

Learning purpose

In any enquiry the focus for teaching, or learning purpose, may alter. In some cases the focus can be on the skills and strategies (processes or 'know how'); in others it may be on what is found out (content or 'know that'); and in yet others there may be a mix. Children need to experience a range of enquiry forms. The topic of drying clothes, for example, can be focused on process skills as in Box 7.

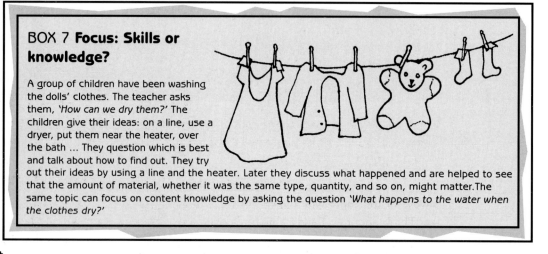

BOX 7 Focus: Skills or knowledge?

A group of children have been washing the dolls' clothes. The teacher asks them, 'How can we dry them?' The children give their ideas: on a line, use a dryer, put them near the heater, over the bath ... They question which is best and talk about how to find out. They try out their ideas by using a line and the heater. Later they discuss what happened and are helped to see that the amount of material, whether it was the same type, quantity, and so on, might matter. The same topic can focus on content knowledge by asking the question 'What happens to the water when the clothes dry?'

Informed adult

Young children need an informed adult who can recognise the potential for science in many activities and has a framework of science knowledge, pedagogic knowledge and knowledge of the conditions for young children's learning. All these frameworks are critical if the adult is to be able to provide and recognise opportunities for problem solving, enquiry and investigation. Probably the most important knowledge is about the children themselves and how they see things. As Athey (1990) has shown, young children have 'persistent concerns', and close observation and interpretation of their activities can help us provide explanations that not only fit their ideas and experiences but also extend those ideas and encourage them towards explanations that are scientifically robust and en route to accuracy. However, young children do need to be taught and to practise skills.

Enthusiasm

As in all curriculum areas children need to be treated seriously and enquiries need to be filled with enthusiasm. Children need an adult who will respond to their questions and concerns in a way that, as Harlen and Jelly (1992) show, turns them into potential investigations. They need an adult who is able to say (particularly when the adult is not sure or does not know) 'Let's find out!' They also need to know what they know, to be conscious of what they have learned, and be proud of their achievements.

Getting started: audit your environment

It is important to identify where in the children's working environment, enquiry is most likely to take place and what sort of content and process issues may arise. Some examples are given below. For each one ask yourself: Does this happen? If not, could it happen? If not, what do I need to alter (routines, resources, etc.) to make it happen?

The context for learning	Opportunities for different types of enquiry
Construction	properties of materials, rigidity, stability, fragility
Sand/water	how liquids and solids behave, sieving (filtration), dissolving, forces – floating and sinking, moving things, bubbles, properties of materials
Creative play/junk modelling	solids and liquids, dissolving, mixing paint, viscosity in liquids, properties of materials
Cooking	heating, cooling, melting, dissolving, mixing, change, healthy eating, variety of foods
Garden	planting, growing, seasonal changes, mud pies
Outdoor large play	pushing and pulling, the friction of surface, weight, use of wheels
Mid-morning snacks, packed lunches, school dinners	health, hygiene, types of food, raw and cooked food

Getting started: plan your role

Step 1: Know your own aims and role

It is not enough just to set up the environment and expect children to educate themselves. Education is about informed intervention. This means the adult needs a framework for thinking about enquiry and for ensuring that the children carry out a balanced and broad range of enquiries. Use the three-phase model of *getting started*, *keeping going* and *looking back* in thinking about your provision:

● Audit the range of experiences children get and ensure that the adult interventions are not always of the same type (types of question, support).

● Think about and audit children's overall experience by considering how open-ended each enquiry is and whether enquiries offer scope for the children to take varied control – do the children always just do the doing and not much of the noticing and framing questions, testing, explaining, etc.?

'It's big girl's work ... these are the bits to make it pretty ... It's a helicopter machine.'

● Identify aspects that individual children find easy/ difficult. This can inform future work with the children. Devise strategies to help and support in new contexts. Observe the children and question your own knowledge of each child, their skills, how they prefer to operate, think... Build more complete profiles.

● Reflect on and discuss what individuals and groups of children have done. This allows us to 'go with the flow but know where the flow is going' and to ask questions that encourage children to reflect on their enquiries with particular educational purpose.

Step 2: Plan the focus of the enquiry

● Clarify whether the primary focus is to teach the children how to enquire or to learn through enquiry.

● Plan in advance how open ended or closed an enquiry is to be. Decide how much of the enquiry to hand over to allow more scope for decision-making when the children are dealing with experiences, resources and topics about which they are more knowledgeable.

⬤ Think about the type of support that the children may need and ensure that it is provided.

Step 3: Know the limitations

If the topic is new, or difficult to you, or if the children are new, it may help to keep more control until confidence is developed. This is an extension of the point about knowing where your starting point is and the children's starting points. The drying clothes example in Box 7 requires the adult to have concepts of evaporation if the content focus is chosen, and that some of the children's explanations of what happens to the water, such as 'it disappears' or 'it goes away', are less specific than terms such as 'it drips off' or 'it goes into the air'. Equally, less-experienced children may need prior experiences if they are not aware that clothes will dry.

Step 4: Plan to keep it going – intervention

In any form, or phase, of enquiry a real issue for the adult is when, whether and how to intervene in the process. A heavy-handed approach to the sand tray example (Box 2) is for the adult to wade in with explanations about air cooling and falling sand. For many children, particularly the pre-5s, this would result in a quick move to another activity! In the primary setting, the equivalent can be equally speedy mental disengagement!

Another adult strategy is just to let the activity happen and then, at its apparent conclusion, get the children together to describe what they have found, with the adult putting their explanation in at the end. This explanation is what the adult wants to focus on from the enquiry. In this case the adult is controlling the 'looking back' and, unless sensitively done, may be focusing on aspects that are not the children's central concern. If this strategy is adopted the adult faces the problem of the children, having finished their enquiry, no longer being interested or remembering what they have done.

A lighter touch is to 'join in' and facilitate the enquiry at the sand tray by suggesting the connection between moving sand and air cooling it (*'I wonder if ...?'*). We have to live with this being taken up or ignored, but it does have the benefit of leaving the previous strategy on the agenda.

'They're seeds ... I'm putting them in my picture.'

Which strategy is chosen depends on the adults' knowledge of the children involved, their knowledge of the possible underlying science, the time available, and so on. Intervention is based on knowledge and wisdom about these children and their starting points. In general, perhaps we can say that with young children adults should:

⬤ go with the flow – see the world as the child represents it and work to extend their knowledge and thinking;

⬤ know where the flow might be going – so you can offer appropriate language and help children make connections between different experiences (*'so it's like ...'*, *'remember when ...'*);

⬤ seek to ensure success for children in their enquiries.

Step 5: Plan the organisation

With very young children many of their enquiries may be individual or alongside others, but with older children the setting is more likely to be in groups. The same principles apply to this work as to all group work: children need to have a shared purpose, time to talk through who will do what, time to become a group, and time to talk about what they have done. Any other educators in the room should be clear about the purposes of the enquiries and what their role is.

Step 6: Plan to look back and celebrate what the children do

If children are to become conscious of what they have learned rather than simply know what they did, they need good feedback and discussion on their science. They need to talk about it as this makes it valid in the eyes of the children, helps them to recollect and reflect on what happened, helps them to learn from others, encourages talk amongst themselves and with adults at home. It is not sufficient to comment on the product of the enquiry: children must be made aware of how they got there, and what they learned about the process and during the process. In any follow-up recording, the process needs to be recorded as well as the product.

Finally

There isn't one 'right' way to teach enquiry. Children learn about the benefits, the processes, the attitudes and skills that are involved from:

- hearing about the enquiries done by others (see Chapter 4);
- watching an adult model being an enquirer/doing an enquiry;
- hearing adults explaining and teaching enquiry processes and skills;
- explaining their own enquiries and the processes and skills involved;
- being helped to make connections between enquiries in similar and different contexts, topics, timescales, group/social situations, purposes, etc.;
- being treated as serious enquirers who want to find out about the world and are prepared to use all their abilities and resources to do so.

However, if young children are encouraged to enquire and experience degrees of control in their enquiries they are, we suggest, more likely to become citizens who are ready, willing and able to join the scientifically literate community.

Sue Ellis and **Sue Kleinberg** are senior lecturers in the Primary Education Department of Strathclyde University, Glasgow. Whilst sharing interests in young children's learning, pedagogy and science, Sue Ellis has a specialist interest in language teaching and Sue Kleinberg in teacher education and enquiry learning. Both teach on undergraduate and postgraduate courses and are currently involved in extensive consultancy and teaching on early intervention for practising teachers.

Chapter 4

Children's language in science

Rosemary Feasey

Adult: That's a great echo you have just made.
Child: Yes, I can make a better one.
Adult: Wow! That was good. So how do you think an echo works?
Child: Oh! You would ask me that. Go away while I think about it!

As adults we take for granted the language we use on a daily basis: exploring ideas, sharing experiences, explaining thoughts by talking to someone else. Young children are at the beginning of this process, learning the words and conventions that are second nature to adults. We are sometimes in danger of forgetting how challenging it can be for children to express themselves, especially in relation to ideas and experiences that are new to them. Children need time to explore their ideas, choose their words and formulate the sentences that explain their thoughts and experiences. The child creating the echo called for 'time out' in order to construct a response: a lesson for adults to be patient, to give children time and support.

Equally we should not underestimate the enjoyment young children experience in using language, the pleasure they get from 'playing' with new words, teasing peers and adults with riddles and hearing themselves speak.

Young children have a lot to learn. They have to master everyday speech and its conventions but they are also expected to learn at school the language of, for example, mathematics, art, PE and, of course, science. Offered to children with patience, care and appropriate support, learning to converse in 'science' can be fun and intriguing. Science 'conversations' open doors for children to think differently about the world and use different ways of working.

Starting points and development

What language abilities do young children possess?

In order to understand where we want to take children in terms of language development we need some understanding of what abilities they already possess. The majority of children come to school or nursery with extensive language abilities and therefore the teacher must ask a series of questions:

- What experiences have children had in relation to science?
- What language structures do the children possess?
- What scientific language do children use (e.g. push, melted, electric)?
- What is the extent of children's everyday language abilities?
- What ideas do they hold in science?

You will notice that none of the questions work from a negative viewpoint; each one acknowledges that children enter school with experience of the world, albeit widely differing from child to child. As professionals, we should not start from a language deficit point of view, but aim to use and add to children's existing language abilities, encouraging them to explore and explain scientific experiences.

Many 4 year-olds have already mastered some of the complexities of language use and possess an ability that:

- is similar to adult speech;
- allows them to understand and express themselves using complex sentences;
- allows them to adjust their speech to suit listeners. (Think about how a child addresses the teacher as opposed to a parent or friend.)

However, the 4 year-old still has a lot to learn and, as Smith and Cowie (1991: 289) indicate, they still have linguistic systems to perfect, such as:

- pronouns;
- auxiliary and regular verbs;
- ability to ask a range of questions.

For example, in Box 1, the children are very expressive but still need linguistic, as well as practical science experience.

Developing children's language in science

Donaldson (1978: 15) suggests that we need to be clear about how we would like children to develop their language in science with our guidance. We would like them to:

- be able to use scientific vocabulary appropriately;
- enjoy scientific language;
- communicate their ideas and experiences in science;
- be articulate, eloquent, expressive and fluent when communicating their science.

Desforges (1989: 43) suggests that:

one of the major tasks of early

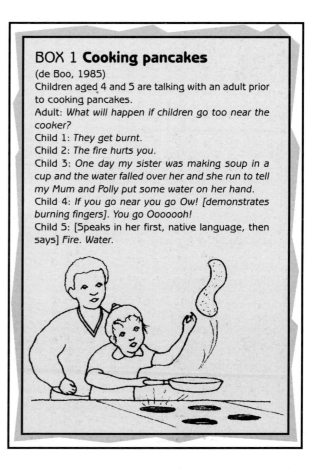

BOX 1 Cooking pancakes
(de Boo, 1985)
Children aged 4 and 5 are talking with an adult prior to cooking pancakes.
Adult: *What will happen if children go too near the cooker?*
Child 1: *They get burnt.*
Child 2: *The fire hurts you.*
Child 3: *One day my sister was making soup in a cup and the water falled over her and she run to tell my Mum and Polly put some water on her hand.*
Child 4: *If you go near you go Ow! [demonstrates burning fingers]. You go Ooooooh!*
Child 5: *[Speaks in her first, native language, then says] Fire. Water.*

'It's sticky and soft – like cream.'

childhood education is to manage the transition to concepts whose powerfulness depends upon their detachment from direct experience.

The challenge of language development in early years in science is threefold:

● to introduce language that is directly related to immediate, concrete, everyday, hands-on experiences;

● to move children on, so that they are able to use the same scientific language in a wider range of contexts that are removed by time and space;

● to develop scientific language that is conceptually based, that is, linked to ideas which may be difficult to understand, for example, movement of particles in dissolving and changes of state.

In order to do this young children need to begin with concrete 'hands-on' experiences that the teacher links to the language of science. This involves focusing on individual scientific terms as well as the sentence structures and question types that help children to give names to objects and experiences, and to explore and explain their understanding.

It is important that children develop the language of science. Scientific language is precise and specific and, as Bearne (1998: 128) suggests:

Whilst it can be argued that everyday words might offer the simplest explanations there are times when a single scientific word can have a particular meaning ... Where children are able to use such words, sentences may be less cluttered and children are then able to develop more accurate scientific concepts.

For children to become proficient in using scientific language, they need to be given the opportunity to learn the linguistic tools and frameworks for talking and writing about their scientific experiences (Feasey, 1999).

It's hard, soft, like a rattle.

A cardigan. It's very soft.

A tablet bottle because it's squeezy.

It feels like soft and hard. It has little arms and legs, some eyes and a nose – it's a teddy bear.

It's soft, tickles – a nappy.

Something squeezy like a toy.

It's made of plastic ... baby bottle.

Children's comments from a 'Feely Box' activity at Chater Infant School

They need to develop objective language and ideas such as 'red', 'heavy', 'evaporate' and 'float'. They need to develop their 'storying' skills (see Chapter 3) into describing and explaining skills.

Children also need to hear the teacher and other people using different types of language in science.

Types and uses of language

Scientific language for objects and events

Children need to learn the scientific language for objects and events. The scientific names of objects are relatively easy to teach children: objects are concrete; they can be held and used and names can be attached to them both verbally and in writing, for example as labels. Children can physically explore objects such as a kaleidoscope, hand lens or plastic tubing, feeling their shape, the material they are made from, using them and experiencing the effects of using them. Here our role is to introduce children to the scientific names and the words that help to describe the concepts and experiences associated with the objects or event. For example:

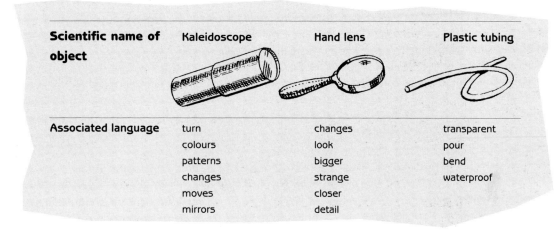

Scientific name of object	Kaleidoscope	Hand lens	Plastic tubing
Associated language	turn	changes	transparent
	colours	look	pour
	patterns	bigger	bend
	changes	strange	waterproof
	moves	closer	
	mirrors	detail	

Adults are central to this language development. Our role is to help children to make connections between the object or event and the word. Simplistic though this might sound, it is an essential feature of science. Even more important, are the steps the teacher takes to ensure that making these connections becomes part of the everyday language use of individual children. This means transferring the responsibility for using the language from the adult to the child. In order for this transference to succeed, we must challenge children to use the correct scientific terms. We do this by encouraging children to use scientific words, offering praise when they do so and making the acquisition of this language fun, for example, through using games, rhymes, riddles and songs. The following example illustrates how learning scientific terms can be fun. It is taken from a song which teaches the names of parts of a plant and is sung to the tune of 'The Wheels on the Bus'.

The roots on a plant grow underground,
Underground, underground.
The roots on a plant grow underground,
Roots are part of a plant.

The stems on a plant hold up the leaves,
Up the leaves, up the leaves.
The stems on a plant hold up the leaves,
Stems are part of a plant.
(Goldish, 1996: 31)

Language to develop scientific concepts

Children also need to master the language that enables them to describe their ideas or conceptual understanding in science: concepts relating to ideas such as forces, movement and electricity. The development of this language raises some fundamental issues in science.

Some early-years educators are uncomfortable about introducing terms such as force, dissolve, or gravity to young children. They question whether children should be exposed to language for which they have not, as yet, developed understanding of the concepts. Some people are concerned that exposure to formal scientific language at an early stage might lead children to develop a range of 'misconceptions' (alternative ideas). Others suggest that this is a form of linguistic censorship and that children encounter these words in a range of situations and will begin to make some sense of them regardless of the teacher.

What is important is that we appreciate that the concepts underpinning this language often take many years to develop and that children will hold many 'alternative ideas'. However, for the majority of children these 'alternative ideas' are a transitory phase through which they pass as they develop ideas that are scientifically acceptable.

Exposing children to scientific language and continually helping them to challenge and refine their understanding of terms is an important role for the teacher and other adults working with young children (Box 2).

BOX 2 **Melting butter**
(de Boo, 1985)

Child: *Look what's happening! The butter on my pancake's dissolving.*

Adult: [thinking how to challenge 'dissolving'] *How can you tell?*

Child: *It's going all runny.*

Adult: *Oh, yes, you're right. It's melting all over.*

During the early years of formal education children are placed towards the beginning of a continuum of developing ideas and experiences, which at this stage we might call 'naive'. As children are increasingly exposed to a range of language and experiences in science, their ideas develop. This in turns helps their language development and their movement towards becoming expert in the use of scientific words to describe objects, phenomena and ideas. Over time, children move from being 'naive' users of language, with no understanding of a scientific term, to being 'expert', able to manipulate words in different contexts, both immediate and concrete, as well as removed from the concrete by time and space:

Naive	Novice	Expert
unfamiliar	familiar	confident
exploratory	repetition	manipulative
everyday	semi-scientific	scientific

The language of science skills and processes (enquiry skills)

There is a third type of language in science that children need to be exposed to: the language of 'doing' in science (see Chapter 3), which supports the development of skills and processes. This is frequently associated with the links between cause and effect, the relationships in science. For example:

If we do this what will happen?
If we change this then ...
I think that will happen because ...
The more you ... the longer the ... will be.

It is important that the teacher, when planning science activities, identifies the scientific language which he or she intends to develop with the children. In Box 3, the teacher planned a science activity on 'change'. As part of the planning process, she identified the language that she thought could be developed through the activity. The discussion also illustrates a group of children moving from naive to novice in their use of language; they know some scientific terms and are beginning to use them. The children also exhibit the ability to link cause and effect in their conversations.

BOX 3 Making biscuits

The teacher planned a science-based cookery session where the children would make biscuits with a chocolate covering and jelly. As part of her planning she listed the learning outcomes for science and the language that she thought should be used to support the development of scientific knowledge and understanding. The highlighted words in the children's responses indicate that the children were using some of the words identified by the teacher as well as other scientific terms. However, these also indicate that the children require more experiences which expose them to those words not yet within their vocabulary.

Language to be developed:
change
cold
crystals
dissolve
empty
full
hard
heat
hot
liquid
melt
mix
powder
set
smooth
soft
solid
transparent
wet

'The flour is like powder – its floaty.'

Children's responses:
When the chocolate melts it will turn into chocolate milk shake.
*It will go **soft**.*
*It will go **runny**.*
*It will go **sticky**.*
*When it's cold it will go **hard**.*
*Boiling water makes it **melt**.*
*Sometimes milky bars **melt** if you don't eat them.*
*The jelly **disappeared** and made the **water** go red.*

*It will go **hard** and **wobbly**.*
*The sugar **disappeared** into the butter.*
*It's **steaming**.*
*I can't taste the **difference** between the raspberry and strawberry.*
*It **sticks together**.*
*If we put them all in we should get some **different** coloured jellies – green, orange, yellow, blue – and see if they taste different.*
*When you put it in the **oven** it goes **soft**.*

The responses in Box 3 suggest that the children require more experience of some of the words so that they become part of their everyday scientific language. There are also interesting uses of language. For example, the children are beginning to make statements relating to cause and effect:

Boiling water makes it melt.

When you put it in the oven it goes soft.

Children are also beginning to use that language of cause and effect in terms of predicting what will happen if they do something:

If we put them all in we should get some different coloured jellies – green, orange, yellow, blue – and see if they taste different.

The expert child is one who has begun to develop 'metalinguistic frameworks', that is, they have the ability to think about and manipulate the language that they are using in science. Indicators include children who:

● demonstrate a knowledge of grammar;

● use their knowledge to construct sentences;

● use language appropriate to the social context;

● recognise and use scientific language appropriately.

Opportunities and contexts

At every stage in the science process, language skills can be developed to assist the learning of science and vice versa. Language is integral to the science cycle, and having a context in which to use language is essential to improving language skills.
(Sherrington, 1993: 206)

Early-years children require constructive practical activities and therefore access to a range of active, hands-on experiences in the classroom. The early-years classroom has enormous potential for developing scientific knowledge and understanding and ways of working, as well as many opportunities for developing scientific language. This requires imaginative use of each of the following areas:

- role play;
- construction;
- sand;
- water;
- book corner;
- technology area;
- imaginative area;
- outdoor play.

Each area provides opportunities to:

- model scientific language;
- explore scientific language;
- practise using scientific language in familiar and new contexts.

In order to realise that potential, we need to ask ourselves the following questions when setting up each of the areas:

- Which science-based learning outcomes could be developed in the area and what kind of science activities?

- How can the area be used to extend children's experiences in science?

- How can each of these areas contribute to the development of children's language and specifically scientific language?

- How can the area be created in partnership with the children and give them ownership?

- Will a visit, for example, to a veterinary surgery, provide children with background knowledge and understanding that they could draw upon to help create the role-play area and enhance experiences?

- What kind of clothes, props and other resources will support and enrich children's experiences and therefore language?

- How can the area be sustained over several weeks? How will new items and activities be introduced at different stages to maintain interest.

'This is our house. It's very dark inside 'cos there's no light'.

'I am making a tunnel ... it keeps falling down, it's too dry'.

● What is the range and progression of language to introduced and developed?

● How can older or more experienced children be encouraged to be role models for younger or less experienced children in the area?

● How can the teacher ensure that the science learning outcomes identified are achieved and the language developed?

In Box 4, the children are using a range of everyday language and also making some interesting comparisons, for example, that the water pouring through the holes is like *'a spider'* and *'rain'*. Offering different objects with a range of challenges and problems, for example, *'How can you stop the water?'*, will help to ensure that the water area remains interesting and moves children's experiences and language forward.

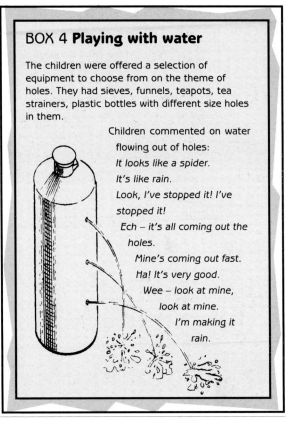

BOX 4 **Playing with water**

The children were offered a selection of equipment to choose from on the theme of holes. They had sieves, funnels, teapots, tea strainers, plastic bottles with different size holes in them.

Children commented on water flowing out of holes:

It looks like a spider.

It's like rain.

Look, I've stopped it! I've stopped it!

Ech – it's all coming out the holes.

Mine's coming out fast.

Ha! It's very good.

Wee – look at mine, look at mine.

I'm making it rain.

Speaking and listening

Observe and value silence

The use of language does not always have to be oral: listening to the silence children offer, for example by watching children engaged in a 'silent' activity, is an essential part of teaching science. Even when children are not putting into words a scientific experience, complex thinking processes may still be taking place.

In some contexts children will be relatively articulate and in another completely silent, with little outward appearance of being able to communicate. We should consider this as the 'language of the mind', children thinking through a situation but not articulating their thoughts through speech. We can 'listen' to them by watching.

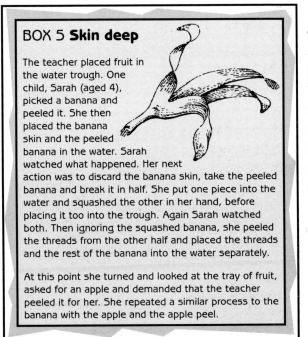

BOX 5 **Skin deep**

The teacher placed fruit in the water trough. One child, Sarah (aged 4), picked a banana and peeled it. She then placed the banana skin and the peeled banana in the water. Sarah watched what happened. Her next action was to discard the banana skin, take the peeled banana and break it in half. She put one piece into the water and squashed the other in her hand, before placing it too into the trough. Again Sarah watched both. Then ignoring the squashed banana, she peeled the threads from the other half and placed the threads and the rest of the banana into the water separately.

At this point she turned and looked at the tray of fruit, asked for an apple and demanded that the teacher peeled it for her. She repeated a similar process to the banana with the apple and the apple peel.

Sometimes children engage in exploration that is self-contained and silent; again, it is important that we should not assume a lack of language. The question is, 'Does the context require adult intervention and the imposition of verbal language on the child and his or her activity?' It might be that the activity lends itself to solitary exploration or that the child is engrossed in his or her schema. At the other extreme, the relationship between peers and child or adult may not support verbal interaction.

In Box 5, 4 year-old Sarah is engaged in a solitary activity at the water trough. The teacher observing decided that adult intervention was inappropriate.

Sarah carried out a structured exploration to find out whether the different parts of the fruit would float or sink. She did this in complete silence and with intense concentration. She followed a set of personal procedures, including actions where she made her own changes and kept some things the same, as well as comparing events. Just as important was the fact that her actions with the banana were repetitive and she then transferred the whole exploration to a different fruit, repeating actions and processes carried out with the banana. Sarah was in fact carrying out quite a complex 'fair test' type investigation, for which repeated tests are essential.

Listening to what children say is important but, equally, the teacher should 'listen' to what children do not say, since this can be just as illuminating. Sometimes children give important clues as to what they do or do not know when they leave out words or stop talking. 'Listening to silence' is an approach to be cultivated with young children.

Readiness to use language

Sometimes children will avoid using words that are not within their linguistic framework. In fact, some children will actively discard or ignore words offered by an adult if they have no understanding of the word or reason to use it. This in itself is a positive move; it indicates to the teacher that the individual requires much more informal exposure to a word and opportunities where scientific terms are 'scaffolded'. Scaffolding words, by using an everyday equivalent alongside a scientific one, is an important approach to language development in science: for example, using the term 'see through' alongside 'transparent'. Children are offered both terms and eventually, when the teacher considers that an individual is ready, the everyday term can be discarded in favour of the scientific one. Of course, children will do this themselves; when they feel confident with a scientific term they will use it in preference to the everyday one. However, we will always need to challenge children to make the transfer from the everyday to the scientific (Box 6).

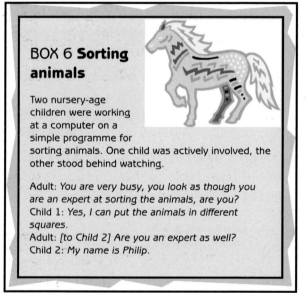

BOX 6 **Sorting animals**

Two nursery-age children were working at a computer on a simple programme for sorting animals. One child was actively involved, the other stood behind watching.

Adult: *You are very busy, you look as though you are an expert at sorting the animals, are you?*
Child 1: *Yes, I can put the animals in different squares.*
Adult: *[to Child 2] Are you an expert as well?*
Child 2: *My name is Philip.*

In this example, Child 1 was confident with the word 'expert' and happily responded to the teacher's question. Child 2, who did not know the meaning of 'expert', changed the conversation, the implied response being 'I don't understand that word and therefore the question, so I am going to say something that I do understand'.

Developing collaborative talk

An important element of developing language in science and also for developing scientific ideas is offering children opportunities for collaborative talk. Vygotsky (1962: 125) recognised the power of discussion. He suggested that language is a tool for thinking and is characterised by a set of complex interactions, rather like:

a continual movement back and forth from thought to word and from word to thought. In that process the relation of thought to word undergoes changes ... thought is not merely expressed in words; it comes into existence through them. Every thought tends to connect something with something else, to establish a relation between them. Every thought moves, grows, develops, fulfils a function, solves a problem.

BOX 7 The melting snowman

Adult: *Look at the picture and think about what the children are saying. Who do you think is right?*

Child 1: *I think that the snowman will melt.*

Child 2: *I don't, because it's cold.*

Child 1: *[to Child 2] But the snowman has got his coat on, right. So he will be warm and melt. Your coat keeps you warm doesn't it?*

Don't put the coat on the snowman – it will melt him

I think it will keep him cold and stop him melting

I don't think it will make any difference

Concept cartoon (from Keogh and Naylor, 1997)

What is the role of the teacher, other adults, indeed other children in this process? Children need to articulate their ideas and other people are an important part of that process in science. As children hear their own ideas, they often begin the process of reconstruction, rephrasing their sentences, adding more information and sometimes correcting themselves. In this process children also respond to the reactions of other people to what they say. Children also refine their ideas in relation to how ideas and experiences described by other people fit into their own framework (Wray and Medwell, 1994).

Collaborative talk, where children and the teacher explore and refine ideas together, is a powerful tool in the classroom.

An excellent strategy for initiating and developing collaborative talk is the use of concept cartoons as created by Keogh and Naylor (1997). The cartoons can be used to encourage children to engage in discussion and debate in relation to everyday situations, as in the example in Box 7 of a snowman melting.

Children refine their ideas according to a range of experiences, both concrete and increasingly conceptual, as they develop their understanding in science and become more linguistically adept.

An important element of language development is the need to challenge children, both in terms of the vocabulary they use and what they think. Concept cartoons do this but challenging children to explain their ideas is generic to teaching young children.

Science for science's sake?

Most people are comfortable with the idea of 'art for art's sake' but few would recognise the idea of 'science for science's sake'. Sometimes the experience offered in science is so interesting and intriguing to children, that language development, quite rightly, takes second place to what is happening, as is seen in the example in Box 8. The children offered only limited language because they were so engrossed in watching and exploring the mixture.

BOX 8 Cornflour mix

The nursery nurse offered 3–4 year-olds an experience with cornflour mixture (when cornflour is mixed to a paste with water it has unusual, surprising properties). The cornflour mix was placed in a baby's bath and the NNEB allowed the children to handle the mix from initial flour to paste – once the water was added. Children were intrigued by the texture of the paste and how it could be moulded and then dripped through their hands. When the nursery nurse turned the bath carefully on its end, the children expected the mixture to pour out but were amazed to watch it slowly move down the bath.

'We are writing
what we did.'

Although the adult used words such as sticky, dry, ball and roll, the experience was so fascinating that the children were 'in awe' of what was happening and could only offer 'oohs' and 'ahs'!

The most appropriate time to discuss what happened with the children was later that day, during circle time, when the teacher could ask children to recollect what happened. Away from the excitement, the adult and the children could explore the language to describe their experiences with the cornflour mixture.

Progression

Language study should start from what children can do, from their positive achievements in language and from the remarkable resources of implicit knowledge about language which all children possess. (Carter, 1991: 4)

The role of the teacher is to recognise children's starting points in language and relate these to the needs of developing children's knowledge and understanding in science across early-years education. The panel below suggests what that progression might be across the early years in science.

Conclusion

The role of the early-years educator is to ensure that the complexities of language are unravelled in order that children can access the richness and excitement of sharing science with other people. Developing children's ability to communicate in precise and appropriate ways should help to unleash the vast knowledge and experience that many children hold despite their tender years. It will also provide firm foundations for success in science education in later years.

Rosemary Feasey is a lecturer in primary science education at the University of Durham. She has been a primary teacher, a deputy head and an advisory teacher for science and has held the prestigious post of Chair of the Association for Science Education. She has researched and written about a range of issues in primary science from investigative work and effective questioning to industry links and literacy in science.

Progression in language development in science

3–4 year-olds
- children describe what they see and what happens;
- children sequence what they talk about;
- children use everyday words;
- teacher introduces some scientific words.

4–5 year-olds
- children use everyday language;
- teacher continues to introduce scientific words which build on those introduced earlier;
- children are encouraged to use scientific words;
- scientific words are displayed around the classroom.

5–6 year-olds
- children retell experiences using a limited range of scientific words;
- children explore their own ideas and those of others orally;
- children begin to talk about cause and effect;
- teacher continues to introduce scientific words linked to class topics.

6–7 year-olds
- children describe events and ideas in detail;
- children begin to offer explanations for what they observe happening;
- children use appropriate scientific language in context;
- children are able to relate cause and effect in science;
- children begin to use language of reflection.

Chapter 5

SCIENCE 3–6

Science through everyday activities

Pauline Boorman and Maggie Rogers

Watch what I can do !

Annie (aged 4) swings upside down on the bar.

Feeling positive is the best condition for learning to take place ... it makes what we all learn more productive and rewarding and is more likely to make us get up and do more. (Wetton and Cansell, 1993)

Phrases such as 'Look what I can do!', 'Watch me!' and 'I can do that too!' will be familiar to those working with young children as they explore their surroundings and demonstrate their latest achievements. There is a sense of excitement, wonder, pleasure and satisfaction associated with the accomplishment and each child is developing confidence and learning about their capabilities. Looking around the early-years classroom, whether nursery, reception or year 1, it is possible to see some children building an ever taller tower with the blocks, some manoeuvring wheeled toys as they push or ride around obstacles outside, others fascinated by

'It's a train. It's got to be like that to be a train. That's where the driver sits.'

the elusive reaction of a ball as it rebounds from the wall. Children will be sifting wet sand, blowing bubbles in the water, trying to solve the problem of how to transport big blocks to the carpet, or standing still, watching the crane on a nearby building site.

What is happening cannot be tied to one particular curriculum area. Some adults (even some governments) make distinctions between subjects or areas of experience and regard them as discrete areas to be taught separately. However, in the early years, by focusing on opportunities for the *subject* we may detract from the numerous possibilities that lie in everything the children do. On some occasions it is almost impossible to classify the experience the children are having as being just science, PE or art. Yet children will be developing their understanding of scientific concepts, with each activity they engage in. Any divisions, actual or imagined, are more the result of adult expectations or government requirements than the way children understand or learn (Moyles, 1994). The types of activity illustrated in this chapter exemplify the holistic nature of learning and the importance of quality play experiences for young children. Although sometimes dismissed as 'just playing' (Moyles, 1989), where play is seen as the opposite to work, playful experiences are shown to be essential in developing children's scientific understanding.

Science in everyday experiences

Children acquire scientific, technological and practical knowledge through their everyday experience, for example:

- in their homes;
- in the classroom or playground;
- travelling by bus or car;
- visiting the shops or local park;
- watching the digger in the roadway.

Scientific knowledge can be developed through these everyday experiences, through other curricular activities, such as design and technology and physical education, and through children's self-chosen play activities. Although, most early-years educators would agree that children are learning in a holistic way, we need to ensure that the learning in science is a focus when appropriate. We need to be aware of two main perspectives (illustrating these with reference to D&T and PE):

- the type of science concepts that arise in play and in everyday experiences, e.g. pushing and pulling, swinging like a pendulum, rotation, speed, friction;
- technological and physical play experiences from which one can draw out the science, e.g. creating and observing shadows, experiencing leverage through using a seesaw, constructing using apparatus, materials or kits.

Not everyone has expertise in science but we all bring our own strengths, specialist subject knowledge and experience to our teaching. What we can all do is consider how children think and learn and how their understanding of science might develop through a range of different experiences. There are learning experiences that encourage similar, transferable skills (observing, problem-solving, communicating, social and motor skills) and commonalities in processes of thinking (predicting, speculating, evaluating). Thus there are many opportunities where scientific learning is being acquired on a minute-by-minute basis every day.

Learning through our bodies

Initially, young children's ideas about science tend to be gained by using their bodies and their senses. Children acquire ideas about science and scientific principles, about themselves and what they can do, in a physical way – for example, by putting things in their mouths and handling objects, turning upside down on a bar, jumping down steps, squeezing through a barrel – long before they have been introduced to concepts and principles formally. *It is important not to under-estimate the significance of physicality.* Children need to get to know their own bodies and what they can do and how their bodies work; they need to feel the cold of the metal frame and the sponginess of the landing mat. In the same way children begin to know how things work by 'experiencing' technology; for example, experiencing the weight of the seesaw as they move up and down, using the force of pushing down on the ground to propel themselves into the air, arranging and re-arranging furniture in the den, deciding how they want it to be.

The adaptations and adjustments tried and tested by Annie in Box 1 were not verbalised but internalised. Either by accident or design

BOX 1 **The climbing frame**

Annie, aged 4, was observed developing a sequence on the climbing frame. It was clear that she was exploring different possibilities as she repeated her actions many times, trying over and over again to drop down between the bars, to clamber along the high ladder, to spiral down the pole. At first she moved along inch by inch but as she persisted she developed the confidence, strength and coordination to carry out her sequence. Delighting in her new-found achievement, she called out '*Watch what I can do!*' and proceeded to give a demonstration. She repeated the movements in the same way until she felt confident enough to try something different.

something different happens or a slight variation causes an unexpected reaction. As children explore possibilities and find out what can be done with their bodies and with the equipment, it becomes obvious to the observer that they are also learning to cope and interact with various aspects of their environment such as gravity, materials, weather, space and surfaces.

Learning by solving problems

Exploring the materials of their world through physical manipulation is also of central importance. Three year-old Jessie, making a papier mâché mask, notices the 'sogginess' of the paper as he prods it with his brush full of paste. Five year-old Zaid is frustrated with his dough as he tries to make it 'spiky' so that it resembles his dad's chest, when making his 'gingerbread dad'. Zaid is also joining limbs of dough on to the torso and trying to make them stick. Bruce (1992), writing about the Block Play Project, suggests that '*the manipulation and exploration of materials leads to novel use of those materials and problem solving – the stuff of the inventor'*. Problem-solving is a widely used term which should not be confused with the 'making' that is heavily directed by adults. Children need to be given opportunities to set up their own enquiries, determine their own problems to solve and come up with their own solutions. In this way *'knowledge ... at its origin, neither arises from objects nor from the subject, but from interactions – at first inextricable – between the subject and those objects'* (Piaget, 1969).

As children manipulate planks and boxes to construct dens, rearrange apparatus to create spaceships or slide cars down the plank to race them, they are developing their awareness of motion, space, gradients, angles and forces, and the properties of materials. They are also developing social skills in cooperation, taking turns, sharing, helping, teamwork and working as a group as they experiment, explore and investigate. They talk and listen, instruct and negotiate, express delight in their own progress and praise others.

In these self-chosen activities we can observe children thoroughly engrossed and immersed in what they are doing. They are solving practical problems in a range of different contexts and living what they are learning (Isaacs, 1974). In this context, play is an essential tool for learning, as they take control and develop solutions to the problems that arise naturally in their play. They are utilising what Vicky Hurst refers to as the *'dynamic force and creativity of play'* where children are able to manipulate and internalise aspects of the world they are familiar with, developing their understanding and working out appropriate responses (Hurst, 1997). The *'play context allows the learner the freedom to experiment without fear of expensive or potentially embarrassing error'* (Anning, 1994: 70).

Everyday experiences such as pushing a trike, sweeping the leaves from the path or stirring the cake mixture can help to develop children's learning in a holistic way. Adults can foster the child's desire to see whether, for example, they can push/ride/roll the trike up or down the slope, develop their understanding of why some trees lose their leaves, or notice the changing texture of the cake mix. Through providing the time, space, opportunity and resources for these to happen, interacting with them and building on the experiences children have brought to the situation (Outterside, 1994), adults can support and challenge children's thinking.

Skills and attitudes

There are skills and attitudes common to science, physical education and design and technology. The earlier examples show children's *curiosity* in action. The children *asked questions* as they *noticed* what was happening to the paper and paste as it dried on the radiator over a period of a day. Children are experiencing first-hand, investigative learning and, at the same time, developing their gross *motor skills*, control, hand–eye coordination, gripping, holding. The group of children constructing their 'den' are taking part in a joint venture, having to *organise* themselves and *communicate* their intentions through language. Together, they are *making decisions* about which apparatus to use, how to lift or carry it into place and where to put it. Such negotiation can develop into the skills of *planning* and *describing* their actions to others. The children with the planks and blocks demonstrate a whole range of skills that they are learning through their play opportunities:

● cooperation, taking turns, sharing, helping, teamwork, working as a group;
● experimentation, exploration, investigation;
● maths – weight, measures, quantities, balance, gradients, angles, speeds, velocity;
● science – travel, knowledge of materials (properties), forces – gravity, light/heavy, gradients, resistance;

- organisation, communication, social interaction, language;
- gross motor skills, control, hand-eye coordination, gripping, holding, lifting;
- constructing, building, designing;
- problem-solving, decision-making;
- patience;
- observing, learning from others;
- safety, being careful.

Contexts

The provision of meaningful contexts is vitally important in stimulating children's active involvement in the learning process. Carry out an audit of your environment – does the context enable the children to think, to do things, to make decisions for themselves and to take control? These will be the contexts that allow the children to develop skills and that provide opportunities for challenges (e.g. 'what happens if ...?') that make sense to the child. The contexts should not only enable them to use their existing intellectual skills but allow and support them to extend and develop those skills to meet new challenges (Blenkin and Kelly, 1996).

It is not always necessary to create a specific environment. Physical play and designing-and-making activities provide a rich context for science to be experienced. The gingerbread figure – discussed, modelled on paper and constructed – provided a real and meaningful context for the children to learn about and develop their understanding of:

> ### BOX 2 **Down the mine**
>
> Nursery children were learning about materials. A mine (a concept familiar and local to the children) was created in the classroom. The inside of the mine was enclosed in fabric to shut out a certain amount of the light and the children were allowed into the 'mine' (only four at a time) wearing crash helmets and carrying torches, spades and trowels. They went in to mine metal (shiny, coloured foil paper) and, on finding it, weighed it and made jewellery with it (rings, bracelets). The activity was extended to the design of a treasure trail in the school garden with children bringing pieces of foil back. Within this context the children were physically engaged in moving in and out of a confined space and designing artefacts. They were engaged in role-play which captured their imagination and extended their learning.

- how materials behave when you mix them together;
- how to make a mouldable material by mixing water (liquid) with flour (powder);
- how to make a solid by heating a mouldable material (achieving a chemical reaction).

The adult's role

As children move through the primary school there is increasingly less opportunity for a playful approach to learning. However, in any number of 'informal' settings – constructing (and often knocking down) the tower of bricks or experiencing the force of gravity when using the slide – children are learning holistically through the involvement of their whole selves. Physical, sensory, cognitive and social experiences all combine and contribute to their understanding. What is learnt is not explicit, often cannot be expressed or even articulated. This means that adults have a crucial role to play in furthering the development of the concepts, skills and processes which the children experience, especially in practical-based activities.

Adults can support and enhance children's understanding of science through everyday activities and occurrences by focusing on the following essential principles:

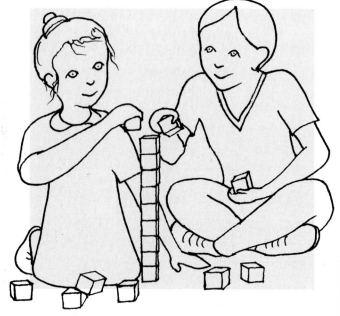

- Start from what children know and can do.
- Provide resources that will interest, engage and stimulate children.
- Give children time to make connections and assimilate new experiences.
- Know when to intervene ... and when *not* to intervene.

While these principles have been itemised, they are also interrelated. We need to encourage, help and empower children to try new and unfamiliar activities and to use their ingenuity and inventiveness. We need to provide sufficient, stimulating resources that allow for individual outcomes.

Resources, however, are not enough. Children also need time to internalise their experiences. A fine balance has to be found between adult intervention and time for the children to meet the challenges being presented by that experience.

Following the children's lead

'Starting from where the children are' may be a familiar phrase but why is this important and how do we know what children know and can do? How do we know where they are at in their learning?

Vygotsky (1978) believed that play showed children operating at the highest level of which they are capable, so if we are concerned to develop their potential we need to provide them with the opportunities to lead or take control of the activity. Our observations can tell us what the

BOX 3 **Designing and constructing**

A nursery teacher set up a table with Mobilo along with some leaflet designs showing aeroplanes. Bethan (aged 5) chose to make the aeroplane design and successfully managed to assemble the pieces. Other children showed interest and made their own models so an adult extended the activity by putting out yellow and red felt-tip pens to match the coloured pieces of Mobilo. She encouraged the children to design their own models.

Some models were quite sophisticated; for example, there was a hinge on one of the drawings. Afterwards they all discussed the models, the adult using familiar vocabulary (wheels, wings) and introducing new words such as *propeller*, which they looked up together in a dictionary.

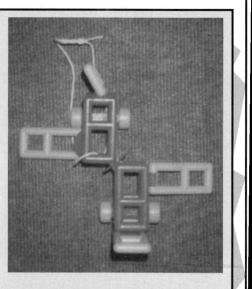

The children were learning about structures and colour, forces and mechanisms and scientific terminology. They were using language purposefully, making independent decisions and cooperating with others in sharing resources.

BOX 4
Driving a car

A nursery nurse was observing a group of children thoroughly absorbed and involved in fantasy play 'driving a car' but the limited resources put constraints on the children's play. The adult encouraged and extended the play by bringing out tyres from the shed. The following day teachers brought out 'A' frames and a steering wheel which the children quickly added to their play vehicle. On another day the children expressed the desire to feel closed in *'like a real car'* and a blanket was draped over the structure.

The children were exploring structures and forces, light and darkness, and shapes. They made decisions and negotiated resources.

children's interests are, how they respond to the resources provided, and how to follow their lead in extending their play (Box 3). Observing also allows us to assess children's starting points in terms of knowledge, skills and independence.

The adult in the Box 3 example inspired the activity and chose the initial learning purpose: designing and making. However, subsequent adult intervention followed the children's lead. By observing the children the adult could decide when it was appropriate to interact and intervene to develop and extend the children's experience. In this situation, the adult and children learn together – neither is seen as the 'expert' and the children learn to be confident when they 'don't know what to do' (Holt, 1965).

Resources

In Box 4 the teacher's choice of resources influences the range of science-related experiences to which the children have access. In the case of the mine (Box 2) the intention of the teacher was for the children to learn about metals but the children gained much more as they explored the darkness of the enclosed area with their helmets and torches.

The children in the example in Box 4 were provided with resources that offered cognitive conflict and challenge, encouraging the children to think and question and find new connections. Resources offered out of their usual contexts, such as a picture showing a zebra in a poppy field or a plastic elephant in the water tank, have the effect of generating questions about knowledge and understanding of our world.

Selecting limitations on resources will also stimulate thinking. For example, as MacLeod-Brudenell suggests (1998), when children are given resources for 'making', offering a *limited* range of tools and components with a *wide* range and variety of materials to experiment with and explore, can be more productive than overwhelming children with too many experiences to choose from.

Time

Without time to get involved, to make connections, internalise and make sense of what is happening, children will not necessarily move their understanding and skills on to the next stage. Providing enough time and knowing when to intervene is vital when children are engaged in self-chosen activities. Research by Bruner (1980) and Mathews (1996) shows us that *'activities tend to be prolonged, extended and developed by a child far more when there is an interested, responsive adult close by who supports, consolidates and affirms what the child is doing'* (Mathews, 1996: 174).

Intervention – the right question at the right time

Asking questions when children are engaged in an activity can challenge their thinking and help them to clarify their intentions as in Box 5. Zoe's rationale for building the walls high was to protect the pig from the wolf, as *in her own experience*, foxes regularly visit her garden at night.

Interacting with individual children as in Box 5 can help them make sense of the

> ### BOX 5 **Building a farm**
>
> Zoe wanted to 'build a farm'. She arranged blocks into a rectangular shape to house a cow and the manger. An adult asked, *'Where will the pig live?'* Zoe then built a barn for the pig, referring to 'long' and 'medium size' blocks and, realising that she needed a doorway, built two towers of bricks. The adult asked, *'How is the door going to open and close?'* Zoe demonstrated by swinging the towers apart and outwards from the doorway – illustrating a hinge mechanism. She added, *'Opens like that. Must do it higher – if wolf eats the little pig … at night foxes and wolves and bears.'*
>
>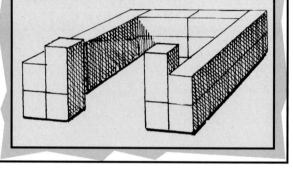

world while their play and/or practical experiences provide the context which is personally meaningful for them (Katz, 1977). By providing relevant questions alongside stimulating resources, the teacher is able to present the children with an environment that supports or 'scaffolds' their knowledge development (Vygotsky, 1978; Bruner, 1980; Hughes, 1986).

We also need to encourage children to think of their own questions and problems to solve (Tizard and Hughes, 1984; Harlen, 1996). If we ask 'the right question at the right time', we offer a good role model as 'curious questioners' ourselves and show that questions can prompt creative exploration. Sometimes, *even one* question is enough to challenge ideas and suggest alternative action, as in Box 6.

> ### BOX 6 **Swinging round the pole**
>
> One day Ming (aged 4) was swinging round and round the pole of a climbing frame. A nursery teacher asked, *'Can you make your body go round the other way?'* At first Ming couldn't do it. She thought a bit and had a try but ended up coming straight down the pole. The next try she managed half a turn and after that a good spiral. She was proud of herself.
>
> Ming was learning about her own body, about gravity and structures. She was gaining self-confidence and independence.

The importance of a balanced curriculum

With the present emphasis on 'back to basics' and the concentration on literacy and numeracy, curriculum time is at a premium and the freedom for children to explore, experiment and experience their physical world is in danger of being severely constrained. 'Work *versus* play' arguments result in a polarisation of academic versus practical skills, as if it were a choice of one *or* the other (Moyles, 1994). The value of the more practical activities in early-years education is inestimable. Anning (1994: 6) insists practical experiences are necessary for a child to become *'a whole balanced person'* as children need to *'use both kinds of skills and related thinking'*.

The centrality of *informal* and *practical experiences* in the early stages of development should warn us against the dangers of too great a formalisation too soon. The activities described in this chapter are rich in opportunities for developing scientific knowledge and understanding and yet are not unique events. The adult's role is fundamental in supporting children by providing resources, time, intervention and understanding, while taking every opportunity to use everyday encounters and play situations to help children see the relevance and excitement of science in their daily lives and to realise that it is integral to almost everything they do.

Pauline Boorman is a specialist in physical education with a particular interest in the early-years curriculum. Her principal concern is to encourage teachers and parents to recognise the important role of physical experiences in the education of children. Pauline is the physical education course leader for student-teachers (undergraduate and post-graduate) at Goldsmiths' University of London, and she writes on this and early-years education.

Maggie Rogers has taught in primary education for many years and now coordinates initial teacher education courses in primary design and technology at Goldsmiths' University of London. She is particularly interested in the links between science and technology and has published research on this subject both nationally and internationally. Maggie is committed to helping student-teachers to develop their understanding of these two areas and the distinctive contribution each makes to the early-years and primary school curriculum.

Chapter 6

Assessment in the early years

Brenda Keogh and Stuart Naylor

> *Does the rain do the vappor [sic] thing before it touches the ground when it is really hot?*
>
> **Simon, aged 4**

Can't I just give them a test?

Science learning in the early years is about curiosity and wanting to know how and why. It is about really seeing something for the first time such as the star that you can find inside an apple. It is about being so fascinated by something that you want to touch it and watch it and return to it time after time. It is about being so excited about what has happened that you want to tell everyone about it. It is about being interested in your ideas and those of your friends and your teachers. It is about wanting to understand more about the world in which you live and about learning how to do that. If assessment is to have any value in any early-years context it must make all of this more likely. We should therefore look at assessment from the point of view of what it can do to enhance the experience of learning science.

It is very tempting to resort to testing as a quick and simple solution to the assessment of children's understanding in science. After all, isn't that what ultimately happens at a national

'What's the white stuff? It's all slimy and sticky – yuk!'

level in order to assess science? To begin to make sense of why we shouldn't just give young children tests in order to assess them in science, we need to consider the relationship between assessment, teaching and learning.

Assessment, teaching and learning are not separate processes, although it helps, at times, to identify what is significant about each of these aspects. Assessment is often described as part of a simple teaching cycle as shown in Figure 1.

This representation of the teaching process appears to separate teaching and assessing. Assessing in this model could indeed be a test that is given at the end of a block of teaching. You teach, you test, you decide what the children do not know and then you teach again! It

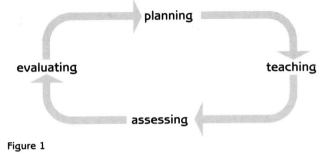

Figure 1

seems straightforward. However, this is not what effective teachers do. Good teaching involves more complex relationships. It may look more like the process shown in Figure 2.

The focus of this model is learning. Teaching, learning and assessing are integrated.

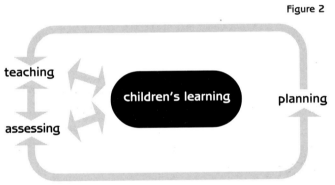

Figure 2

Judgements about children's learning are made as the children engage in everyday activities and teaching is adjusted accordingly. In this way opportunities for assessment also provide opportunities for learning and vice versa. Assessment is not just about what children can recall in a test or what they reveal at the end of an activity, it is also about challenging children's thinking and developing understanding of science. This more realistically reflects what teachers normally do to support learning although it is not always recognised as assessment.

As teachers we have access to a world of developing ideas that children hold. These ideas and the way they develop can be fascinating. Young children can surprise us with the power of their thinking and how they respond when they have their scientific ideas challenged. Carrie (aged 3) in Box 1, learning about sliding and rolling, captures the potential quality of thinking of young children engaging with science. She shows why assessing scientific understanding can be so rewarding.

Unfortunately, some of the approaches to the assessment of science seem to convey the view

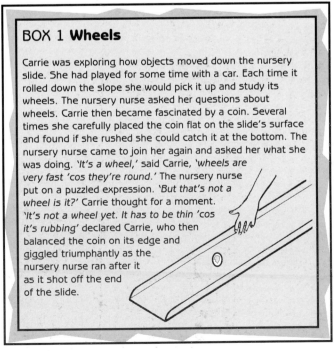

BOX 1 **Wheels**

Carrie was exploring how objects moved down the nursery slide. She had played for some time with a car. Each time it rolled down the slope she would pick it up and study its wheels. The nursery nurse asked her questions about wheels. Carrie then became fascinated by a coin. Several times she carefully placed the coin flat on the slide's surface and found if she rushed she could catch it at the bottom. The nursery nurse came to join her again and asked her what she was doing. 'It's a wheel,' said Carrie, 'wheels are very fast 'cos they're round.' The nursery nurse put on a puzzled expression. 'But that's not a wheel is it?' Carrie thought for a moment. 'It's not a wheel yet. It has to be thin 'cos it's rubbing' declared Carrie, who then balanced the coin on its edge and giggled triumphantly as the nursery nurse ran after it as it shot off the end of the slide.

that science is only about the learning of facts and that our role as teachers is to ensure that those facts are in place to be revealed on demand. This is an understandable development in a climate where tests and accountability dominate. However, this has led to the over-assessment of certain types of learning and to criticisms of the assessment process. In her writing about assessment Wynne Harlen identifies these concerns:

Assessment in education has been criticised for interfering with learning, the analogy being that of a gardener constantly pulling up his plants to see if the roots are growing. There is some truth in this, particularly if there is too much assessment of the wrong kind, but it also distorts reality to make a point. Gardeners do have to find if their plants are growing and they do this, not by uprooting them, but by careful observation with a knowledgeable eye, so that they give water and food at the right time and avoid either undernourishment or overwatering. (Harlen, 1983: vii)

Wynne Harlen's analogy helps us to see that assessment is not just about testing learning. Knowing children's ideas not only enables us to plan for the future but also enables us to challenge and enthuse children through an immediate response to what they do and say. Her ideas confirm the view that assessment is a natural part of what we do in our normal interactions with children rather than an add-on that can disrupt their development. If our 'plants' are to grow in their scientific understanding, more than scientific facts are required. If we are to achieve our learning goals, the focus for assessment in science will be as much on the development of attitudes, such as curiosity and collaboration, as on the understanding of the content.

Isn't assessment for adults only?

Assessment is not only about teachers learning about children. It is also about metacognition, that is children learning about their own learning. Brown *et al.* (1997) point to children's limited awareness of their own ideas and of their own ability to learn. If science is about developing ideas then it would seem appropriate for children to be aware that they do have ideas. If children are to enjoy learning science they need help to recognise the value of their own ideas and encouragement to be active in the learning process. In reviewing studies of learning in infant classrooms, Tricia David notes the impact of children's active involvement in the assessment and learning process:

In guided play situations, where the children take the lead in making decisions about their learning activities, there is a much closer 'match' of challenge and child. (David, 1996: 98)

The teacher's role of scaffolding learning through discussion, questions and the provision of materials is seen as significant in such situations, again pointing to the importance of the judgements made while interacting with children actively engaged in science.

Barnes (1976), in his study of groups, noted the impact of individual ideas on the thinking of the whole group and pointed to how important it was to encourage the sharing of ideas. This can enable the teacher to make judgements about the children's understanding. The children can also make judgements about each other's ideas and this can trigger new thinking, as in the example in Box 2.

The need to explore and investigate comes from the differences which exist between ideas. If everyone has the same idea there would be little need to find out more. Making situations problematic, by revealing to the children that there is more than one possible view, is an important stimulus in science. By revealing a range of viewpoints within a group, assessment can provide a purpose for scientific activity. In this way assessment can become much more than simply testing learning in order to record what it is that children know.

Gaining access to young children's ideas

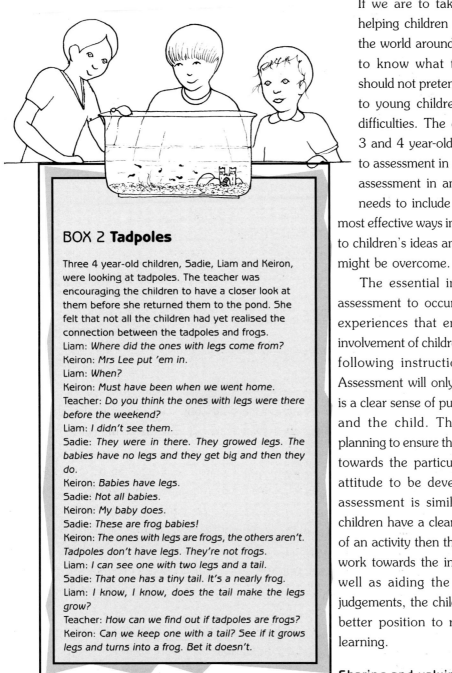

BOX 2 Tadpoles

Three 4 year-old children, Sadie, Liam and Keiron, were looking at tadpoles. The teacher was encouraging the children to have a closer look at them before she returned them to the pond. She felt that not all the children had yet realised the connection between the tadpoles and frogs.

Liam: *Where did the ones with legs come from?*

Keiron: *Mrs Lee put 'em in.*

Liam: *When?*

Keiron: *Must have been when we went home.*

Teacher: *Do you think the ones with legs were there before the weekend?*

Liam: *I didn't see them.*

Sadie: *They were in there. They growed legs. The babies have no legs and they get big and then they do.*

Keiron: *Babies have legs.*

Sadie: *Not all babies.*

Keiron: *My baby does.*

Sadie: *These are frog babies!*

Keiron: *The ones with legs are frogs, the others aren't. Tadpoles don't have legs. They're not frogs.*

Liam: *I can see one with two legs and a tail.*

Sadie: *That one has a tiny tail. It's a nearly frog.*

Liam: *I know, I know, does the tail make the legs grow?*

Teacher: *How can we find out if tadpoles are frogs?*

Keiron: *Can we keep one with a tail? See if it grows legs and turns into a frog. Bet it doesn't.*

If we are to take a positive role in helping children to learn more about the world around them then we need to know what they think. But we should not pretend that gaining access to young children's ideas is without difficulties. The egocentric nature of 3 and 4 year-olds can create barriers to assessment in science. Planning for assessment in an early-years context needs to include consideration of the most effective ways in which to gain access to children's ideas and how these barriers might be overcome.

The essential ingredient to enable assessment to occur is the provision of experiences that encourage the active involvement of children rather than merely following instructions from an adult. Assessment will only be effective if there is a clear sense of purpose for the teacher and the child. This requires careful planning to ensure that teaching is directed towards the particular skill, concept or attitude to be developed and that the assessment is similarly focused. If the children have a clear idea of the purpose of an activity then they are more likely to work towards the intended outcome. As well as aiding the teacher in making judgements, the children will also be in a better position to reflect on their own learning.

Sharing and valuing ideas

Children who are unwilling to communicate can be problematic. Early-years teachers are used to working patiently with children who seem slow to reveal their own ideas. Patient support is important when trying to encourage children to put forward ideas about the world. We need to realise that young children may be reluctant to share ideas because they have not explored the ideas before or have not previously tried to express scientific thinking. It is wrong to assume that silence means lack of understanding, as Benny in Box 3 demonstrates.

Sometimes children's inability to form the right words makes the meaning less clear. It may have been difficult to make sense of the words of Simon, aged 4, who introduced this chapter. However, in the context of a discussion about where puddles have gone, and knowing that Simon had recently visited a very hot part of the States, the meaning becomes excitingly clear.

Children need to feel encouraged to put forward their ideas and to feel that their limited communication skills and vocabulary are not a barrier to them sharing their ideas. It is easy to conclude that children's ideas are insignificant and in some way rather quaint. Lansdown (1996:

BOX 3 Floating and sinking

Benny (aged 4) and friends had been exploring floating and sinking for several days. There had been plenty of discussion about what the children had observed. All the children shared their ideas freely except Benny who had stood on the outside of the activities and said very little in response to questions. Had Benny learnt anything from the activities? The teacher found it difficult to decide. A few days later the floating and sinking activity was introduced for a new group of children. Benny watched from the painting table. Tom played with a jar. He was trying to make it float but each time he put it in the trough it filled with water and sank. Eventually Benny left his painting, came over to the water trough, found a lid which he adeptly screwed on to the jar and placed it in the water. 'See, float!' he said.

75) feels that 'children's views are still, for a substantial proportion of the adult population, often treated as ill informed, irrational, irresponsible, amusing or cute.'

It is essential for children to feel that they can openly play with their ideas, test them out, have them respected and taken seriously. They can be bewildered when a serious comment or an action draws laughter or is treated in a patronising manner. They should feel that we enjoy and respect their ideas. In that way a climate of sharing of ideas, which is so important to assessment and learning in science, can begin to be created.

Effective questioning

Although some of the problems of gaining access to ideas are due to the age and inexperience of the children, others are of our own making.

In order to find out ideas we often ask questions. If direct questions can be intimidating to adults, how much more so will they be to children? Person-centred questions, such as, when finding a dead plant on the windowsill, 'Why do you think this plant stopped growing?', are much less threatening than subject-centred questions, such as 'Why did this plant stop growing?' (Harlen, 1996). The subtle difference in wording can make a significant difference to a child's confidence in answering. A person-centred question gives a very positive message to the children about the value of their ideas. It also avoids the feeling that there is only one right answer. Too much emphasis on 'right answers' can inhibit children and leave them afraid of being wrong.

Our reasons for questioning have to be because we are genuinely interested in the children's replies. Some children very quickly learn that if you don't know the 'right' answer then there is little point in thinking. As Joan Dean (1992: 86) notes:

It is very easy for children to get the idea that the way teachers ask questions is the norm. Most people ask questions because they want to know something. Teachers are unusual in that they ask questions to which they usually already know the answer.

It is through the questions we ask that the children begin to form their own views of the role of questioning in science. Therefore planning needs to provide a framework for the nature of the questions to be asked. This does not mean listing every question. It means that key questions can be identified in relation to any particular activity. This will help to avoid unproductive questions and provide a focus for assessment.

A group of teachers on an early-years course, who felt that they used questioning effectively in science, were surprised when they listened to tapes of their own questioning. They noted the occasions when important ideas were ignored because they did not appear to quite fit what was expected. It is hardly surprising in these circumstances that novice learners begin to lose faith in their own ideas.

Circle time

Circle time can provide a very fruitful opportunity for assessment in science. As with other uses of circle time, it can help all children feel that their ideas have value. It can also help them to recognise the range of scientific views that their peers hold. Hayton (1995) notes the value of this kind of sharing of ideas and recognises the problem of children who do not engage effectively in discussion. She believes that it is necessary for teachers to share their 'power' with children so that:

teaching ceases to be understood by the children as the process of them finding out what 'answer' we have in our mind ... [through this] the children will begin to share and develop each other's ideas.' (Hayton, 1995: 37–38)

Gallas (1995) focused her research on giving children a voice within her class in order to help them to learn more about science. She points to the need for children to be taught the conventions of talk and discusses how she encouraged the more confident children to see their responsibility for helping other children to share their ideas. Effective socialisation can support effective assessment.

Managing assessment

The more talk we generate about science and the more provision we make for positive experiences of science, the more opportunities we will have to assess children's ideas in science. However, it is worth sounding a note of caution at this point. If assessment is allowed to dominate, so that every time children are engaged in talking about and doing science there is an adult waiting to question them about their ideas, it may become counterproductive. Children could be too occupied with what they are doing to want to talk. They need time away from adults to explore ideas alone or with a friend, without any intervention. It is unnecessary to worry about what might have been seen or heard if only someone had been there observing. Assessment is not about knowing everything, it is about making best use of what *is* known.

Some curriculum guidance and training has led to the assumption that it is necessary to create special activities to assess children. This need not be the case. As Mitchell and Koshy (1995: 37) point out:

If the starting point given to children is rich enough in possible learning outcomes then it will in turn provide an excellent focus for assessment.

Generally, strategies that encourage children to talk about science or to engage in exploration are likely to be effective assessment strategies.

Ultimately, making assessment manageable has to be the goal to strive for. If it is viewed as a natural part of the teaching process then, for much of the time, very little special provision needs to be made for separate assessment. It will be an ongoing part of a three-way relationship between the child, the teacher and the parent. Of course there will be occasional times when the normal interactions will leave us uncertain about a child's developing understanding. In this case we may decide that we need to plan to spend extra time focusing on an individual child. This should be the exception, not the rule, in assessing science.

The nature of young children's ideas

It is in the early years that the beginnings of the big ideas in science are forming, ideas that we take for granted are new to young children. We cannot assume that a child will know that a seed needs water to grow, that the Sun only appears to move across the sky, that some materials let water through and others don't, or that things change over time. It is important that assessment helps to nurture these ideas and aid their development.

If we are to make best use of assessment it helps to be aware of the nature of children's ideas. The range of ideas that children hold have been explored in several research projects. They can be seen in material such as the Nuffield Primary Science key stage 1 *Teachers' Guides* (Nuffield, 1995) which draw on the work of the SPACE research project. Although aimed at a slightly older age group they give some indication of the ideas that early-years children may hold.

Clearly children's experiences are limited, as is their reasoning power. This can lead to the formation of a restricted view of the world in which their ideas appear incongruous to those with a more complete view of scientific explanations. The ideas that children hold are often referred to as 'alternative' conceptions. This implies that they hold a different view of the world from the scientifically acceptable one. Sometimes it is more helpful to view their ideas as 'restricted' conceptions, ideas that are limited in their scope because of the limitations of the child's experience. The purpose of assessment and teaching would then be to recognise the cause of these restrictions to their thinking and to open gateways to more complete conceptions.

Reasoning from experience

Many of the experiences of young children can lead them to believe that the world behaves reasonably consistently. Initially, interpreting how the world works relies on this consistency. Reasoning from this experience can be misleading when trying to understand scientific ideas.

For example, children put coats on to keep warm so from their experience a coat should also make a snowman warmer and make it melt (see page 37). As they begin to try to apply ideas from one context to another it would be surprising if they came to any other conclusion. Assessment can help us to recognise where children are trying to reason from experience and enable us to provide appropriate experiences to help to broaden their understanding through comparing their initial ideas with the outcomes of their explorations. At the age of 4 children may not understand how insulation works but, by being given the opportunity to discuss what might happen if they put a coat on a snowman, they may see that something different from what they expected occurs. In this way they can begin to learn that reasoning from experience is only one part of learning about the world.

Blurring fantasy and reality

Children love to fantasise. We encourage the blurring of fantasy and reality through play and stories, and this is a very important and enjoyable part of learning. We might expect that this blurring of fantasy and reality would lead children to inappropriate conclusions in science. However, we should not be too misled by this merging of science ideas and fantasy. It is not unusual, for example, for children to put faces on their shadows, even when they can explain that shadows are formed by blocking light. For young children scientific accuracy seems unimportant. For them fantasy and scientific explanation can rest happily together.

Amie, when asked '*Where do shadows go at night?*' answered that they get into bed with you to keep you warm. She enjoyed the image she was creating. It was clear that there was a large degree of story-telling on her part, as she knew how to make shadows. Our assessment can play along with, and recognise, this fantasising whilst gently probing below the fantasy to look for the scientific ideas. In this way we can begin to help the children to see that there are times when it is helpful to separate the two.

Common-sense ideas

Science is made more problematic for children because common sense and science sense do not always agree. Once they have learned how to add two and two together they will always make four. Normally everyone agrees with this, at home, at school, and when they go to the shops. It is common sense to believe this. Such consistency is not always so in science. Common sense and science sense can sometimes be completely different. It is not surprising that, when Meenal was discussing pushes and pulls, she said the word *force* means when '*someone makes you do something you don't want to do*'. This is what her previous experience of force had told her. Assessment helps us to be aware of children's common-sense ideas and to develop their concepts into more scientifically acceptable ones. Common sense is very resistant to change. We should not be too disappointed if change comes slowly.

'Squirrelling' or purposeful recording?

Some teachers could be viewed as squirrels who raid children's brains for nuggets of knowledge which they store away until they might be needed. In many instances, just like the squirrels, far more is stored than is needed and difficulty is experienced in retrieving what has been stored. If we return to the learning intentions identified at the beginning of this chapter it can be seen that much of this squirrelling is of little value in achieving these goals.

Yet we are accountable and therefore need to respond in whatever ways help us to feel secure in the current climate. This is likely to involve written records. These records cannot be used to note everything each child does or says. This is not a good use of anyone's time. In creating a system of recording we need to ask why we want to record the information. The normal answers to this question are:

● I want to record this because I want to remember it the next time I teach.

● I want to record this because it is an exciting development for this child and helps to add to the picture I already have.

● I want to record this because it gives me ideas for an activity in the future.

● I want to record this because I want to share this with someone else such as another teacher or a parent.

None of these answers should result in lengthy recording. Records should enable us to focus on what is significant. If all children can do something that we set as an objective then it is unnecessary to note this thirty-five times. Our plans will tell us that it has been taught; our lack of additional notes will tell us that all children appear to have learnt it successfully. The best records are those that are in constant use because they contain information that adds to the process of teaching and communicating with others. If recording is purposeful, the loss of a record book should have some impact.

BOX 4 Puddles

Robin (aged 3) had been exploring puddles. His teacher asked him what he had learnt. *'You know what, puddles disappear! I thought they sinked into the floor but they don't. You know how I know? I put one in a dish and its gone. And it didn't sink in 'cos a dish is hard, see?'* [Robin held up the dish]. *'I don't know where its gone to. Do you?'*

But the greatest value in assessment lies not in the record books but in the day-to-day interactions with children. It is here that the greatest strength of early-years education lies, in listening, responding, challenging and confirming.

Sharing assessments with the children

It is useful to remind ourselves of whose ideas are being assessed. Do children's ideas become *our* property once they have left the children's mouths or once an action has been noted? If we want children to be motivated to learn science by the way we use assessment, then we need always to recognise the original ownership of the ideas. Therefore, what we should do with most of our assessments is to share them with the children and help them to reflect on their own learning. Initially they may not understand what they are expected to do. Given time, they will begin the process of learning how to become involved in the assessment process and how to make decisions about their own future learning.

Three and four year-olds should be at the beginning of a long learning adventure. Some will become our future scientists and some will become our future science teachers; those who do neither of these should still enjoy the experience of learning science. Attitudes to learning are established early. If they only experience assessment of science as 'tests' carried out by their teacher, then they will never learn how important assessment is in taking control of their own learning. They may never appreciate what science ideas are really about. They may never learn how to learn science.

Brenda Keogh and **Stuart Naylor** are both lecturers in science education at the Manchester Metropolitan University Institute of Education, Brenda at the Crewe site and Stuart at the Didsbury site. They each have extensive experience in teacher education as well as experience in primary and secondary schools as teachers, advisory teachers and technicians. They are the creators of the concept cartoons featured in the 'Science on the Underground' project and have recently written a series of Science Questions books for key stage 1 science and literacy published by Hodder.

Chapter 7

SCIENCE
3–6

Promoting equality and citizenship

John Siraj-Blatchford

The most important learning in pre-school concerns aspiration, task commitment, social skills and feelings of efficacy. (Sylva, 1994)

The children we teach differ in many ways: they are boys or girls, black or white, with or without English as their first language, from high-rise flats or farmhouses; they come from families with diverse backgrounds and educational expectations. *Any* stereotyping can be influential and very hurtful but, in particular, 'race' and gender harassment and abuse can have a devastating effect on a child's self-esteem. Early-years educators can do a great deal to safeguard children from prejudice and, as attitudes are acquired as young as 3, early action is vital.

Roberts (1998) cites Katz (1995) in identifying the four major pre-school learning goals:

We need to challenge stereotypes from an early age

- knowledge;
- skills;
- dispositions;
- feelings.

It is absolutely essential that we pay particular attention to children's dispositions and feelings if they are to be successful in acquiring knowledge and skills. If we want children to gain a sound knowledge and understanding of science then we must encourage a positive learning disposition towards the subject. Underachievement, apathy, or even resistance in adolescence usually begins with some degree of discouragement in the early years. We therefore need to tackle 'race' and gender misconceptions and other prejudices head-on.

Science has a very poor record when it comes to social equality. Scientists in the nineteenth century tried to legitimise these inequalities in their theories of eugenics and in the development of biased intelligence tests. Even today, despite progress in many other subjects and fields of endeavour, white middle-class males continue to be over-represented in the physical sciences in schools, in university science courses generally, and in senior positions throughout the various scientific professions. It was a male scientist who first argued that women were genetically incapable of thinking scientifically and it was a scientist who first (mis)applied the category of 'race' to human beings (Thorpe *et al.*, 1994). In fact science may be considered to have had a fairly negative overall effect upon equality in education so that all of these misconceptions need to be confronted at every opportunity.

Identity and education

When we consider the different needs of children we must take into consideration their identity as individuals and as members of various groups.

'Racial' identity

The concept of 'race' endures in education and yet, as Sandra Harding (1993: 8) suggests:
It has now been forty years since some biologists and physical anthropologists began to point out that the concept of race is incompatible with evolutionary theory. ... it turns out that there is greater genetic variation within every 'racial' group than there is between any two of them. Yet scientists in such fields as biology, medicine, and public health still use this ... anachronistic concept of race.

'We are all different'

Unfortunately, racial inequality will continue to be reproduced in the curriculum as long as the common assumption remains unchallenged that 'our' 'developed' high-technology way of life shows that we are superior to 'others'. In fact much of the treatment of history in science and technology education (and in the wider media) tends to support some of the most pervasive racist ideologies. Many, if not, most ethnic majority (white) people have grown up to believe themselves to be culturally (if not intellectually) superior to black people. Their 'common-sense' (yet totally mistaken) everyday observations appear to confirm their prejudices: they see the relative poverty of *so-called* third-world (majority) communities in predominantly scientific and technological terms and they *infer* cultural (and sometimes individual) inferiority (Siraj-Blatchford, 1996).

Until recently, teachers have had little impact on countering this (Troyna and Hatcher, 1991; Wright, 1992). The MacPherson report on the recent Stephen Lawrence Inquiry stated that *'radical thinking and sustained action is needed from pre-school onwards ... with [positive] education and example [given] at the earliest age'* (quoted in Lane, 1999). We *can* change attitudes if we begin with our youngest children.

Cultural identity

Identity can be seen as an educational issue when the needs of bilingual and ethnic minority children are considered. A link has been made between language, culture and identity. The Swann Report stated that:
Membership of a particular ethnic group is one of the most important aspects of an

individual's identity – in how he or she perceives him or herself and in how he or she is perceived by others. (DES, 1985: 3)

In recent years there has been much greater recognition that even children of the same gender or ethnic group often have different identities (Hall, 1992). Identity is increasingly recognised as a much more complex matter, something conditioned by class, gender and many other experiences that are more or less shared by our membership of other groups in society. Some identity-forming categories such as 'ethnicity' may be socially advantageous or disadvantageous to us *in particular circumstances.* This explains why children of different ethnic groups, different genders, or who are differently abled, do not all perceive themselves in the same way. Some individuals may hold contradictory positions, so that we shouldn't be at all surprised to find that some girls develop a keen interest in the physical sciences without in any way compromising their femininity. In the same way individual black and ethnic minority children may be very confident and academically successful in spite of the structural, cultural and interpersonal racism in society.

Gender

Despite all of the efforts of the past two decades, despite an almost universal commitment to the principles of equality of opportunity in education and employment, women continue to do most of the housework in the home. Men continue to see themselves as somehow 'above' tasks such as washing around the toilet. There is a kind of cultural inertia at work here; the domination of women (still) appears to be 'natural'. The 'new man' is considered an aberration, as somehow 'odd' or peculiar, and, like many other misconceptions, these ideas prove to be remarkably pernicious and enduring.

Research by Ross and Browne (1993) revealed that young children identify activities in a gender-related way from a very early age (e.g. girls' toys / boys' toys). Children have already developed different expectations of their roles. It may be that mothers, older sisters, aunts and grandmothers do not provide the kind of positive scientific and technological role-models that brothers, uncles, fathers and grandfathers do. Furthermore, negative technological stereotypes are reproduced and even exaggerated in the media. Science is therefore seen as irrelevant to 'normal' women and girls: *Implicit in much school education and ... gender reform is the notion of 'normal' girls, usually seen to be middle-class and Anglo. Such girls are positioned positively; their culture is made central. They therefore receive an education couched in their own values. Girls who are not positioned as 'normal' are positioned as other than and less than 'normal' girls. They are seen as different from what is normal and preferable, as special or 'at risk'; not because this is how they have been positioned by the schools, but rather because of some sort of dysfunction in their backgrounds.* (Kenway *et al.*, 1996: 250)

Changing expectations

Popular conceptions of ability and intelligence *are* now changing along with public expectations related to social roles and status, our expectations regarding culture, the family and towards employment. An increased effort is being made to promote children's (and teachers') understanding of the nature of science and the involvement and contribution of non-Western cultures in scientific development (Harding, 1993; Reiss, 1993;

Siraj-Blatchford, 1996; Hodson, 1998).

If we are to aspire to a more equal society and interdependent and peaceful world we must recognise and celebrate the scientific and technological achievements of 'third-' and 'fourth-world' cultures and of women. We need to promote the public understanding *of* science and we need to promote a greater understanding of the public *by* scientists. We need to recognise and promote the view that the best solution to a problem is rarely the most complicated and expensive in terms of resources, and that 'feminine' and 'indigenous' ecological and holistic scientific approaches have significant advantages over more 'masculine' and Eurocentric approaches:

We know that the white man does not understand our ways. He is a stranger who comes in the night, and takes from the land whatever he needs. The earth is not his friend, but his enemy, and when he's conquered it he moves on. He kidnaps the earth from his children. His appetite will devour the earth and leave behind a desert. If all the beasts were gone, we would die from a great loneliness of the spirit, for whatever happens to the beasts also happens to us. All things are connected. Whatever befalls the earth befalls the children of the earth. (Chief Seattle, 1885)

Putting equal opportunities into practice

It is essential to tackle misconceptions head-on and this can be achieved by actively supporting young children in the development of their self-esteem and self-identity. For example, children of 3 to 6 years of age commonly exhibit curiosity about physical differences. At this age the children develop their identity as family members and they can also absorb their family's stereotypes and biases. It is also at this stage that children begin to classify people into groups and to develop theories about why people are different. In fact it is at this stage, when they are forming their first friendships, that we can do the most to support them in learning to accept diversity and to feel comfortable with differences. As previously suggested, biologists used to think that human beings could be split up into different groups or 'races', but the study of genetics has now shown that the differences between people within one population are enormous in comparison to any differences that can be found between populations. 'Race' has no biological significance for human beings. The differences that we see between groups really *are* only 'skin deep'.

Self-portrait by Maranna, age 5 years and 10 months

Me and my friends

The following scheme may be pursued with a group of children acting as a 'collective scientist' – with the educator directing the discussion and structuring the activities as they go along. The activities will also provide some preparation for later work on 'Ourselves' (National Curriculum, England and Wales, key stage 1; Environmental Studies, Scotland, P1–P3). Children can be taught about variation and classification, for example:

to recognise similarities and differences between themselves and other pupils; that living things can be grouped according to observable similarities and differences. (DFE, 1995)

We are all the same

Parents, carers and teachers might prepare for the activities by discussing what *'being the same'* means and by brainstorming a list of all the groups of which they and their children are members. Ideas for such groups are likely to include family, gender and religious groups and can be extended to include more subtle groupings such as hair, eye colour, complexion and skin colour. Adults and children can respond to the fundamental question:

In what ways are we all the same?

The discussion is likely to begin with references to physiology (one head, two arms), and this should be encouraged before going on to more subtle similarities such as 'we all eat food' and cultural similarities such as 'we all speak English in school'. The aim is to produce the biggest possible list and this should be displayed prominently and referred to frequently throughout the programme.

We are all different

The next stage is to carry out a series of investigations with the children that explore a number of ways in which they all differ from each other. The examples in Box 1 are provided as suggestions and the investigations should be continued until the children clearly accept (and

BOX 1 **Simon says**

'Simon says' the oldest children in the class are the biggest. Is this true?

'The children draw silhouettes of each other (standing against paper pinned to the wall). The adult puts the age in months on each, displays them on the wall in order, and then asks, 'Are the oldest children the tallest?' and 'What have we learnt?' The conclusions will probably be: 'We are all different heights' and 'We are (nearly?) all different ages'.

Display these along with the findings from each of the following:

'Simon says' there are only three skin colours. Is that true?

Each child draws their face and is supported in mixing paint to match as closely as they can their own skin colour. The pictures are then sorted and discussed. It should be clear that nearly everyone's face is a slightly different colour. They are all beautiful and to say that there are just three colours is rather silly.

'Simon says' if you are bigger you are stronger. Is that true?

The silhouettes can be used again for this and a 'measure' of strength obtained by having the children take turns in pushing on some bathroom scales.

'Simon says' the bigger your hand is the more wooden beads or 'Unifix' you can pick up. Is that true?

The hands can be silhouetted and the number of beads that can be held at once drawn on to them.

'Simon says' that people with longer legs can jump further. Is that true?

Silhouettes of legs can be drawn, cut and displayed graphically on the wall, as in the age/height investigation above, before taking the children out to measure their jumps on the ground with chalk and measuring sticks. The trick is to show the legs displayed as they would look if they were to confirm the prediction first and then line them up according to the measured results (see details in Siraj-Blatchford and Macleod-Brudenell, 1999).

The children can then put together all of their findings and compare themselves with the others: the leg and hand silhouettes can be attached to the body silhouette in a display. The comparisons will stimulate purposeful discussion and literacy.

Socially and scientifically, the aim at the end of the day is to convince the children that **every single one of them is different.**

celebrate) that 'every single one of them is different' (the investigations all show continuous variation – they don't fit into clear categories). Playing 'Simon says' gives a friendly objectivity to the game.

Belonging to a group

As a final activity the children could identify the groups that they belong to in terms of gender, home language, favourite hobbies, favourite colours, favourite pets, favourite food, eye colours, and so on. The children can use these to develop their mathematical knowledge and skills. Venn diagrams can be used to produce displays that show that the groups are usually mutually exclusive – and that the groups that are important to them cut across gender, ethnicity, etc. In a multi-ethnic group of children and parents, inherited characteristics that are *not* related to ethnicity might also be included in this, such as tongue curling and ear lobes.

It's just a fact of nature that we are not all able to curl our tongue up into a U-shape in our mouths and we don't all have droopy ear lobes – if you don't believe it take a look! There is no significance whatsoever in these variations: they are inherited characteristics of no importance at all – just like skin colour!

Extending the theme

Apart from ensuring that we show equality of support and positive attitudes, we could, for example, combine the above programme with staff INSET or an out-of-school/centre parent workshop. This would be a good time to discuss:

● the implications of increased mixed parentage;

● the Children Act and UN Convention on the Rights of the Child;

● the historical and contemporary relationship between so-called 'race' groups;

● the importance of positive role models.

Note: A crucial concept to emphasise in the discussions relates to our tendency to emphasise the *differences* we see between ourselves and 'others' while we take the *similarities* between us for granted. Restore the balance by celebrating the similarities.

Improving self-image: girls and boys

Girls have often been disadvantaged in science education in the past, and boys and girls tend to have different scientific interests, so the child's membership of a particular gender group is extremely significant. In this sense a topic like 'Ourselves' tends to be a fairly gender-neutral subject, but 'Transport' or 'Machines' won't be. We know that girls who often succeed in primary science and technology go on to become discouraged at secondary school and underachieve in science, particularly in the physical sciences (Kelly, 1985; Murphy and Gipps, 1996). Both educators and industrialists agree that something needs to be done about this.

We know that infants soon form strong opinions about the kind of activities that are suited to boys and girls (Ross and Browne, 1993). Boys are often encouraged and girls discouraged in science because of their different experiences with toys and play activities; as children get older these attitudes become linked to job aspirations and life choices in a very limiting way. Selecting neutral topics, and alternating topics such as 'Transport' with 'Homes and gardens', can give a sense of entitlement to both boys and girls.

'I'm making cakes pretty. My mummy makes cakes.'

Observe your children in free play. Who plays mostly with construction kits? What do boys build? Girls? In what kind of play do boys and girls engage in the home corner? Are any toys perceived as more suitable for the boys? What effect does it have if the adult plays alongside? Is it necessary that girls should be more concerned with social interactions and the boys with three-dimensional doing and making?

Seeing ourselves as 'scientists'

We should encourage all of the children in our care to see themselves as aspiring scientists. The products of science are all around us and it is never too early to begin educating our children about it. However you look at it, science is a game with rules. It is also a game that even the youngest children can play.

For professional scientists 'playing the game' means obeying these rules:

● keeping an open mind;

● respecting evidence but always being critical in its evaluation;

● participating in a community that encourages the free exchange of information, critical peer review and testing.

This latter point is crucial because, as Driver *et al.* (1996: 44) put it: *Scientific knowledge is the product of a community, not of an individual. Findings reported by an individual must survive an institutional checking and testing mechanism, before being accepted as knowledge.*

Even the youngest children can be encouraged to play to the rules in the same way and science investigations can be treated, and presented, as forms of play in themselves. We can gradually introduce new tests,

BOX 2 The science corner

Joshua, age 6 [in the science corner]: *Sometimes I pretend to be someone discovering things. Last week I was the first person ever in the whole world to light a bulb! Sometimes though I really do discover something. Like, did you know if you tear a bit of paper you can see hairy things with the magnifying glass? Look, I'll show you.*(Sparks Linfield, 1998)

Making an electrical game

techniques and challenges that can be used in the children's own problem solving. Children may need encouragement to ask questions and, although we may not always know the answers, it is important to legitimise the search for one, that is, to value the children's enquiries (see Chapter 3).

Resources (see Appendix also)

Resources supporting young 'scientists' will include a good selection of reference books and fiction. The nursery or school environment is a great, accessible resource – whether natural or urban (e.g. the supermarket). A mature hedge or tree within, or adjacent to, a garden or nursery setting will support a host of wildlife. It won't take long to find out about the ecology and even a limited familiarity with the names of plants and 'minibeasts' will impress a young child and show them that there are amazing things to learn about in nature.

The importance of adult attitudes

We have a wonderful opportunity to influence children's attitudes but, to succeed, we need positive male and female role models in early-years education and informed adult attitudes to science. Young children will model their behaviour on those who are warm and loving towards them, those who seem to have more power, influence and competence, and those seen as similar to themselves.

In practice this means demonstrating interest ourselves, in such things as plants and 'minibeasts', shadows and rainfall, showing that *we* investigate when we are curious, and that *we* enjoy investigating things for ourselves.

It is particularly important to avoid passing on any anxieties that we may have developed ourselves about science. The key factor in supporting science is the quality of intervention. Even if our own knowledge of science is modest we can create a high-quality learning environment, one that will enhance children's interest and capability in science in the home, in a play group, nursery or infant classroom. A great deal can be done on an opportunity basis, during discussions outside, on shopping trips and outings, in fact anywhere that children engage with their environment. Resources may be limited but the trick is to learn as much as you can about what you have and use these resources to the full.

Promoting citizenship

Children can develop a sense of community responsibility in individual classroom projects, such as designing a toy for a baby or for a child who can't hear very well, or making welcome cards for children and parents who are new to the school (de Boo, 1999).

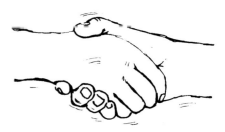

Pre-school centres and infant schools may provide a community focus for local campaigns on, for instance, protecting children's outdoor play environments or providing safe crossing-points in heavy traffic areas. We can use such opportunities to model good practice and involve the children. When children are encouraged to be actively involved in these campaigns they are learning some really important principles of democratic society. They learn about their place in society, their rights and individual responsibilities. Such activities should be extended, in collaboration with parents, as far as possible in the interests of the children's education and of the local community. Examples might include:

- projects concerned with litter and pollution;
- improving safe access to the nursery or school gate;
- reducing traffic and increasing numbers of children who walk to and from school;
- easier access for the disabled to the school, cinema, etc.;
- using the school as a venue for different ethnic arts performances.

All of these projects can be tackled, at different levels, with children from age 3 upwards.

These ideas and intentions need to be written into the policy for equal opportunities, such as the 'Framework for equality' (EYTARN, 1999). Children need a range of resources, not just a token black doll. We need to think and talk to each other about our own assumptions and expectations. We need to demonstrate these positively as we care for children of all different ethnic groups, languages, gender and abilities.

John Siraj-Blatchford is a Senior Lecturer in Research in Primary Science at Homerton College, Cambridge. He is the author of numerous, significant publications about science and technology in the early years. John's research has focused on this, on children's development in general and his enduring interest in values education and the public understanding of science.

Some of the material in this chapter is expanded upon in Siraj-Blatchford and Macleod-Brudenell (1999) *Supporting science, design and technology in the early years*. Buckingham: Open University Press.

Chapter 8

SCIENCE 3–6

Managing science in the early years

Mary French and Audrey Randall

> *Children need space and time for playful exploration, to revisit experiences, practise their skills and try things out for themselves.* (Moyles, 1989)

Learning in science is unlikely to happen if it is not made a special focus in early-years education. Providing the appropriate learning environment to cover the expected curriculum and satisfy the needs of all the children is not an easy task. Add to that the learning objectives for science which a teacher hopes to cover, and the challenge becomes even more daunting.

The imaginative area 'baby clinic' provides a motivating environment for exploratory play

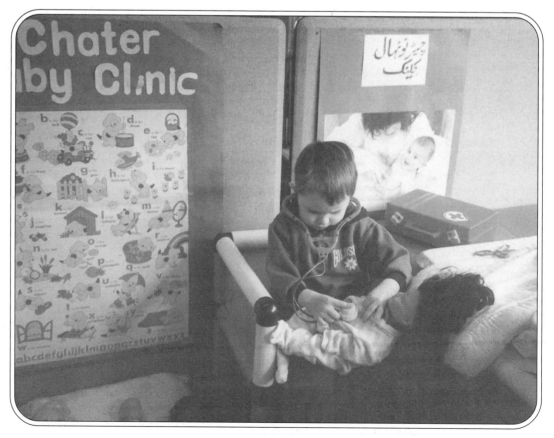

An integrated approach and key science experiences

Setting specific scientific learning experiences within a theme or topic is generally accepted as the most appropriate way for young children to learn. This approach gives more opportunities for the adults working with the children to exploit situations where links can be made. For example, if stories and poems are connected to the activities and experiences in which the children are involved, then the children can be reminded of, and asked to recall, related science experiences. Every opportunity should be taken to reinforce children's learning to make the activity more meaningful.

Nevertheless, in addition to this kind of integrated experience, there are certain key experiences which children should have access to over a long period (e.g. exploring materials, cooking, finding out about themselves, growing plants, building structures, etc.).

There are also key skills. Given the emphasis in this book so far, it may seem repetitious to state that children need time to observe, play, explore, discuss and practise, yet so often pressures from outside make this ideal unattainable. Teachers are constantly reminded to ensure that the 'curriculum is structured' and to 'monitor children's progress' but it is vital that the regime is flexible enough to accommodate the needs of all the children. It is not in anyone's interest to go on relentlessly trying to motivate children if the subject matter is inappropriate or the resources are too restrictive.

Sometimes it is important to have the intervention of an adult but on other occasions it is not. Children need space and time for playful exploration, to revisit experiences, practise their skills and try things out for themselves (Moyles, 1989). Anyone who had observed children will recognise their expressions of delight when they master a skill or solve a problem.

Partnership

Children come from different backgrounds and have different languages and cultures; it is the responsibility of the school or nursery to acknowledge these differences and accommodate them. Parents and other adults in the children's extended family have a right to know what is going on and why certain activities and experiences are provided. It is helpful if information is given explaining the focus of the themes or topics being taught.

For learning in science to be successful it is essential for the adults working with the children to know the purposes of the activities provided and the content of the overall programme. If possible, they should be involved in the planning and implementation but if this is not an option, they should at least have basic information about the topic and the activities being offered.

It is also very helpful if parents and other adults can be given some

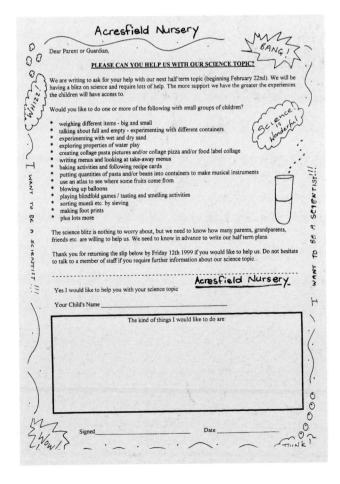

guidance on the sort of questions and responses that might be appropriate (de Bóo, 1999). Over-questioning can be very inhibiting and giving 'right' answers can stifle children's curiosity. It needs a great deal of insight and experience to get this right every time.

The child's point of view

Even with experience, we can never be sure that young children are 'seeing' what we 'see'. All teachers must have experienced the ignominy of taking children through some 'mind-bending' experience to help them learn only to find out afterwards that the children were on a completely different wavelength. On one occasion, after exploring a mango by looking, feeling and smelling, three reception children were asked *'Now what can you tell me about this?'* Darren responded quickly: *'Do you know I've got nipples?'*

On another occasion, a group of 6-year-old children were taken on a visit to a local church. The vicar gave them a guided tour, explaining about the font, the statues, altar and stained-glass windows. At the end of the tour he asked the children whether they had any questions. *'Yes'*, said Emma, pointing to the angelic statues, *'Are them real fairies?'*

Children need ownership over their learning if it is to be of any lasting value to them. First-hand experiences are essential elements in this if children are to make sense of their wonderful, but sometimes confusing world. Books, pictures and posters can enhance their learning but these cannot inspire the awe and wonder that accompanies exposure to reality.

Children's comments reveal attitudes such as awe and wonder:

'Look how beautiful it is out there ... the sunshine, the sky is blue.' Tom

'It looks beautiful 'cos all the flowers are growing.' Anna

'If it's cold and starts to rain you have to stay indoors. If it is sunny it makes me feel really happy.' Taranjit

Planning for science in nursery and reception

The rest of this chapter describes how teachers in one school plan for science in the nursery and reception classes. The planning process has evolved over several years taking into account High Scope Key Experiences (Sylva, 1986), 'desirable outcomes' (SCAA, 1997), the National Curriculum (England and Wales) (DFE, 1995) and, more recently, the need for more explicit systems for monitoring and evaluating the curriculum as education providers have become more accountable.

With all the constraints, the school attempts to fulfil statutory requirements while retaining an holistic approach to curriculum planning that works for the children and staff in this school.

Whole-school planning

All the teachers in the school prefer to use a whole-school topic approach that has been used successfully for a number of years. They decided that these topics should be science-based. While some subjects have to be given extra emphasis, for example literacy and numeracy, the main focus is science and links are made between subjects whenever possible. They have found that science is one of the best ways of stimulating thinking, ideas and skills that can be applied across the curriculum.

Their local education authority science scheme of work 'Steps in Science' was used as a starting point. The staff modified this to enable the whole school to work simultaneously on six half-term topics:

● **Autumn term:** People   Celebrations
● **Spring term:** Buildings and places   Food
● **Summer term:** Out and about   Living things

Working collaboratively, nursery and infant teachers constructed a long-term plan for each subject. Teachers agreed what aspects of each subject would be taught each year, taking into account the time available and possible links with science and the planned topics. Using the long-term plan, teachers in each year group worked together to construct topic plans for each term.

In this school there is an intake into the nursery and reception classes each term. This means children have one, two or three terms in reception class, depending on their date of birth. To ensure that all the reception-year group have similar experiences by the end of the year, the nursery and reception class plan their curriculum together.

Nursery planning for science

In the nursery, the teacher, nursery nurses and bilingual classroom assistant work together to plan the detailed nursery curriculum each term, taking into account the school's long-term plans and recommended early-years learning goals (Boxes 1 and 2).

For example, in the long-term plan for science in the autumn term the children are expected to 'find out about themselves and babies'. In 'desirable outcomes' (SCAA, 1997) they are required to 'recognise some simple features of living things – human' and to 'use exploration to gain skills and emergent knowledge

---

BOX 1

Nursery autumn long-term science plan
● Finding out about themselves and babies
● Exploring materials through a range of senses

Nursery autumn medium-term science plan
(desirable outcomes)
● To look closely at similarities, differences and change
● To recognise some simple features of living things – human
● To use exploration to gain skills and emergent knowledge about themselves
● To talk about observations of objects/events in natural world (human), sometimes recording them

Nursery medium-term science plan – practical activities
● Imaginative baby clinic area (half term)
● Imaginative hospital area (half term)
● Changes to baby: toddler, child, adult
● Naming body parts
● Kim's Game, feely box, observation drawings using items from baby clinic/hospital
● Making baby food
● Adding white paint to water tray = milk, with spoons, baby bottles, etc.
● Testing nappy absorbency
● Push/pull baby toys
● 'I can' e.g. crawl, walk, jump, etc.
● Making individual book with e.g. baby photo, current photo, hand prints, etc.
● Colours of eyes, skin, hair, etc.
● Make baby sounds and record on tape
● Themed water/sand toys, e.g. bath toys, dolls and sponges
● Visitors with babies to change nappy, feed, etc.
● Health visitor/midwife

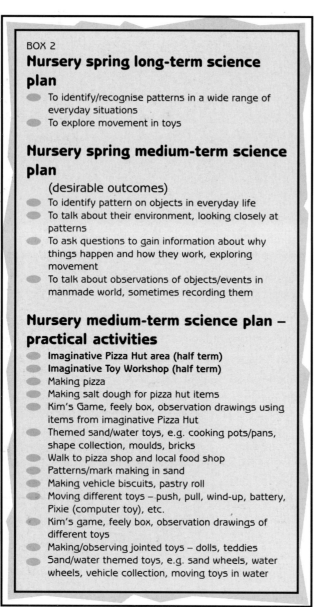

BOX 2

Nursery spring long-term science plan
● To identify/recognise patterns in a wide range of everyday situations
● To explore movement in toys

Nursery spring medium-term science plan
(desirable outcomes)
● To identify pattern on objects in everyday life
● To talk about their environment, looking closely at patterns
● To ask questions to gain information about why things happen and how they work, exploring movement
● To talk about observations of objects/events in manmade world, sometimes recording them

Nursery medium-term science plan – practical activities
● **Imaginative Pizza Hut area (half term)**
● **Imaginative Toy Workshop (half term)**
● Making pizza
● Making salt dough for pizza hut items
● Kim's Game, feely box, observation drawings using items from imaginative Pizza Hut
● Themed sand/water toys, e.g. cooking pots/pans, shape collection, moulds, bricks
● Walk to pizza shop and local food shop
● Patterns/mark making in sand
● Making vehicle biscuits, pastry roll
● Moving different toys – push, pull, wind-up, battery, Pixie (computer toy), etc.
● Kim's game, feely box, observation drawings of different toys
● Making/observing jointed toys – dolls, teddies
● Sand/water themed toys, e.g. sand wheels, water wheels, vehicle collection, moving toys in water

about themselves'. Tasks for the children are organised in two or three blocks. The practical activities done by the children are planned in detail for each week and also take into account High Scope Key Experiences (see Boxes 3 and 4).

Often, an activity has more than one learning objective and these can be relevant to other areas of the curriculum. However, it is important to be clear about which particular learning objective is being highlighted to ensure breadth in the curriculum overall. Choosing to focus on fewer objectives concentrates teachers' observation and listening so that they can 'tune in' and assess children's learning more specifically and evaluate the programme.

For example, the activity on eye colour offered a range of potential learning objectives: counting numbers and sorting into sets, using describing and comparative language, designing and making a collage. The science objectives could include these plus knowledge of the similarities and differences between people. The learning would need to take account of different backgrounds and the need to be sensitive when discussing facial characteristics, etc. (see Chapter 7). As the activity carried on over two or three days, it was possible to select one or two objectives only at any one time.

The practical activities for science are intended to arouse children's curiosity and to encourage them to 'act like scientists'. They provide opportunities for:

● careful observation;

● simple investigations such as making baby food and testing nappy absorbency;

● discussion about the things they did and what they noticed.

Children's records of their work in science

The children are sometimes encouraged to draw what they have seen. **Drawing** is not only a good way for young children to record their experiences, it can be more revealing of their knowledge than a piece of written text (de Bóo, 1999). Apart from encouraging children to think about how to represent objects and phenomena, the children are making marks and developing motor skills. Children's drawings can also be assessed against National Curriculum criteria (e.g. knowledge of 'stem', 'flower'), 'desirable outcomes' (e.g. 'identify features of objects and

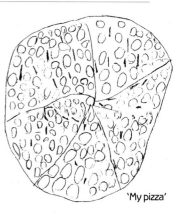

'My pizza'

BOX 3 Short-term science plan: weekly activities (Example A)

TOPIC: Patterns in everyday situations   Week beginning: ....   Group activities

Activity	HSKE (High Scope Key Experiences)	Area of learning	Desirable outcomes	Assessment/evaluation
Making pizzas – cooking	Classification (4d): Using and describing something in different ways	Knowledge and understanding of our world – science	To learn techniques of mixing, kneading dough and to reinforce chopping/ cutting of vegetables	'A very worthwhile cooking activity – making dough, chopping vegetables and cheese – lots to do. Children very enthusiastic following all other pizza-related work. Eaten very quickly!'
Feely box – Pizza Hut items	Language (3b): Describing objects	Knowledge and understanding of our world – science	To identify and talk about shape and pattern in items from imaginative area	'Activity followed Kim's Game using the same objects – meant all children were able to label and begin to describe. Noted several 'shape' words used.'
Observation drawing – Pizza Hut items	Creative representation (2a/f): Drawing and recognising objects by sight	Knowledge and understanding of our world – science	To record pictorially observations of shape and pattern in food/ utensils	'Quality of observation drawing shows marked improvement following language-based activities of Kim's Game/feely box with same objects. Good strategy to remember.'
Kim's Game – Pizza Hut items	Language and literacy and classification (4e): Holding more than one attribute in mind at a time	Knowledge and understanding of our world – science	To 'label' correctly tools and food	'Found children were able to label objects well, having had the opportunity to play with/ explore in imaginatiove area – reinforced by feely box and Pizza Hut activities.'

BOX 4 Short-term science plan: weekly activities (Example B)

TOPIC: Ourselves and babies   Week beginning: ....   Group activities
Materials through senses

Activity	High Scope Key Experiences	Area of learning	Desirable outcomes	Assessment/evaluation
Exploring baby clinic imaginative area	Initiative and social relations (1h): Creating/experiencing collaborative play	Knowledge and understanding of our world – science	To be introduced to baby items by name, uses, etc., for use in their imaginative/ exploratory play	'Good exploratory/cooperative play from beginning – both boys and girls – take photos of imaginative play for display/book.'
Baby milk/milk bottle activity – (adding white paint to water = milk)	Space (7a): Filling/ emptying	Knowledge and understanding of our world – science	To use exploration to gain skills of filling/ emptying/screwing lids on bottles	'Many of the children were more fascinated with mixing white paint into water tray and its effects and changes visually than in the actual measuring/filling – but having introduced this, was used later in free activity time.'
Nappy absorbency test	Language and literacy (3b): Describing relationships	Knowledge and understanding of our world – science	To explore, with guidance, water on nappy materials and talk about what happens	'Was a reinforcing activity of 'heavy/light' following previous weighing activity – showed awareness that water changed the nappy and made it heavy.'
Make baby sounds cassette	Music (10b): Explore and identify sounds	Knowledge and understanding of our world – science	To recognise and make sounds of a baby, recording on to a cassette	'Some children much more confident than others in 'having a go'. Listening to a previous group's tape helped some.'

Child's record of making pizza scribed by adult

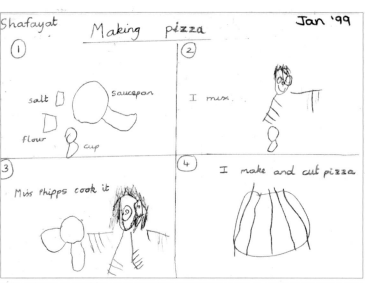

Shafayat   Making pizza   Jan '99

① salt ☐ saucepan
flour cup

② I mix.

③ Miss Phipps cook it

④ I make and cut pizza

Computer record of 'feely box' comments

'It's a plate, hard and round.'   **Tom**
'Menu, 'cos it's made out of paper.'   **Nicola**
'I feel the cutter because it's hard and round.' **Cameron**
'Pizza ... hard ... triangle.'   **Ibi**
'Pizza ... hard 'cos the bits on the lower side is soft and the other side is bumpy.'   **Thomas**
'Tomato is in the box because it feels to me round.' **Zain**
'Cutter because it's sharp... I make it go round and round   .' **Matthew**

Children's computer drawings

Sheraz

Catriona

Babies drawn on Computer

events') and the Goodenough criteria (Harris, 1985) (e.g. 'Draw a man').

Making collages of observed objects or phenomena encourages cooperation and social as well as science skills.

Photographs can record temporary events or children's interests and achievements.

Models such as those made in the 'Toy workshop' are semi-permanent records of their skills and knowledge.

Written records, written by children or scribed for them by a participating adult, can reinforce their language skills and show their developing awareness of structuring language for an audience.

The **computer** can be used for both written and drawn records of children's experiences.

When each activity is completed it is evaluated by the teacher or nursery nurse to inform future planning. The planning and observations are monitored by the Headteacher every two weeks.

Recording and monitoring children's progress

While the children are working, nursery staff observe them and record interesting or significant comments made by the children. These comments show the level of language used, for example sentence structure, use of nouns and adjectives, ability to question and to make connections between things. The children's comments also reveal attitudes such as awe and wonder, recalled memories of the children when younger, imagination and creativity, explanation, planning, reflection and growing mathematical concepts.

Photographs are often included in the records. They reveal children's interest, concentration and cooperation, not only to the staff but to parents and family. The children use the photographs as a diary and a prompt. They describe and elaborate on their experiences and draw their parents into a kind of retroactive participation.

The ongoing records are kept in a record book with a double page for each child for each

Recording of Achievement in the Early Years
(Form to be completed by teachers and shared with the parent and child)

Area of Achievement - Science/Investigative Experiences	Nursery 19 98/9			Reception 19		
	Au	Sp	Su	Au	Sp	Su
LS						
Comments on observations of familiar materials & asks questions eg "This is rough and bumpy"	key	asks questions	–			
Repeats activity to see if it happens again		sand water				
Asks questions about properties of familiar materials eg "Why is this one so heavy"						
Makes predictions about possible outcomes eg "If I.....then maybe............"						
Sustains interest over period of time eg seeds growing, feeding animals, mould growing....						
Can name parts of own body, eg arm, leg, neck, eyes, ears.......	some	fair range				
Can name parts of flowering plants eg roots, stem, leaves, bulb, flower...		flower leaf				
Knows many appliances use electricity. Is aware of the danger						
Plays with & talks about things that can be moved by pushing/pulling eg toy cars up & down ramps, train track play, tricyles, scooters........	play	beg to talk	play			
Cooking	✓	✓	✓			
Nursery garden	✓	✓	✓			
Feely Box	✓	✓	✓			
Kims Game	✓	✓	✓			
observation drawing ①: shape ②?details	S	S+ ②?	–			

Date	Teacher/ N Nurse	Parent/ Guardian	Action/Discussion Points
			* Please note if child achieves statements in first or/ and second language
Su 98	ACJ	Summer Parent Evening ✓	- enjoyed planting potatoes and often looks at garden. - joined in cooking ① chopping fruit, ② mixing dough + rolling, needing some assistance with knife + rolling pin. - Feely Box "little one, do dig" (spade) - kims game - named 4/6 missing minibeasts.
Aut 98	ACJ	Autumn Evening	- has been very interested in activities + is offering more verbally eg "its too →

BOX 5

Date	Teacher/ Nursery Nurse	Parent/ Guardian	Action/Discussion Points
			Please note if child achieves statements in first or/and second language heavy... the water, inside" (nappy testing activity) - Feely Box - "nappy...", "bottle... its got a ..." (mouth sucking action for teat), "bandage because its soft) - Good use of knife to chop vegetable, for soup, fork to mash baby food. - Continues to love garden - planted bulbs + wallflowers. - Observation drawing - shape of baby items. - kims game (as last term)
Sp 99	ACJ	Spring P. Evening	- Continues to offer comments eg "this makes it hard when you cook it" (salt dough activity). - Feely Box - describing in more details "tomato in the box because it feels round". - kims game, named 1/6 + all 6/6 items when missing. - Pizza hut drawing - now showing some details - Asian Cooking Tools + Pizza (see folder) He will enjoy science activities on transfer to Reception + should be encouraged to begin to predict + reason + to record in more detail pictorially.

area of the curriculum (see Box 5). These are collated at the end of each term and recorded in each child's Record of Achievement. The contents are discussed with parents and used to inform individual target-setting and how parents can support this.

There is no baseline assessment for science but the English baseline gives an indication of each child's likely starting point; for example, their knowledge and use of vocabulary. The Record of Achievement is updated each term and monitored by the headteacher.

Making best use of auxiliary people

It is essential that everyone working in or visiting the nursery is aware of the learning plans and objectives. Copies of the weekly and daily plans are available on a board in the nursery for all to read. The teacher also talks to parents and other voluntary helpers before they start.

Nursery nurses are fully involved at the planning stages and contribute to the planning to meet their daily learning objectives. They are fully aware of the important part they play in meeting the teaching and learning objectives.

Students on school placement are given copies of the plans and helped to participate fully and take responsibility for planning and resourcing activities that are part of the plan. They also take on special projects (see below).

Involving parents

Parents are keen to know what children are doing in school. At the suggestion of the nursery teacher, a student helper produced, as part of her course work, a booklet for parents describing what topic work is. The booklets are distributed to all parents and have been translated into Urdu for the bilingual families.

Parents also like to know in advance about the topic plans for each term. Those who wish can plan relevant day trips during the school holidays. Others like to visit the library or purchase books. There is a strong feeling of family participation which feeds into pupils' achievements and a sense of 'family' success.

Parents often come in to help with topic work; for example bringing babies and toddlers to school to show feeding, nappy changing, growth and development. Other ideas for encouraging parental involvement and awareness of scientific objectives can be found in the 'SHIPS' pack (ASE, 1991). This suggests simple activities for children and parents to carry out together in the home.

The value of the integrated approach to science teaching

The staff in this school chose the integrated approach because it allows all children to reinforce their learning. It is particularly beneficial for the many children with English as their second language. The continual planned introduction and reinforcement of new vocabulary and learning experiences through science gives children the time they need to acquire and apply new vocabulary.

Within this approach there is time for children to 'switch off' task, to digress, to talk about their immediate concerns and interests and to explore on their own. All who work with young children have seen the fascination on their faces when watching a snail or seeing their own shadows, their surprise when they see themselves upside down when they look into a spoon, or the 'magic' when their seeds begin to sprout and grow into plants in the nursery garden.

Such experiences are the beginning of science development and these are the things that children remember.

Mary French taught art in a secondary school before moving into primary education. As a primary teacher she became interested in the ways in which art skills can support science. While teaching in Oxfordshire she was involved in the Schools Council *Match and Mismatch* project. Following her move to Hertfordshire she worked for a number of years on a voluntary basis with the Hertfordshire Science Advisory Service. She has an ASE Diploma in Science Education. Mary is currently Head of Chater Infant School in Watford, Hertfordshire.

Audrey Randall worked over a period of 25 years as a teacher and then Headteacher at Brookland Nursery and Infant School in Cheshunt, Hertfordshire, where she was fully committed to ensuring that science was an essential part of the curriculum. She has assisted the Hertfordshire Science Advisory Service in providing in-service courses and was a member of the Science Working Group responsible for the original orders for Science 5–16 National Curriculum. She has served on the ASE's Primary Sub-committee and edited *ASE Primary Science*.

The science plans were drawn up by **Annette James** who worked in infant education for a number of years as a Deputy Head in Hertfordshire and then moved to open up and run a new purpose-built nursery at Chater Infant School in 1990. Annette has a Diploma in Early Years Teaching. While at Chater Infant School she has been involved in a GEST project to raise achievement in bilingual children through the development of science language.

Chapter 9

Planning the future

Max de Bóo

It is apparent that the single most effective means of determining the success of pre-school and primary education, is the reflectiveness of the staff involved. (Dunlop, 1998: 48)

We are at the beginning of a new era. There is an increasing awareness of the importance of providing good-quality education in the early years. Good quality means well-resourced, stimulating environments, appropriate programmes and experiences for young children and well-trained, well-qualified staff. New commercial nurseries are springing up like mushrooms and are endeavouring to meet the high standards established by state nurseries and good playgroups (the largest provider of pre-school education and care in the UK).

Young children need access to good resources

Good-quality programmes of learning

There are Government guidelines advocating appropriate provision for young children (QCA, 1999) and necessary training for teachers of 3–8 year-olds (DfEE, 1998). There is also increasing access to books, commercial schemes and recommendations from reputable national bodies as to what constitutes good-quality learning experiences for the very young. The Pre-school

Playgroups Association endorses the scientific (exploratory, investigative) approach to learning in its booklets (PPA, 1991) and local education authorities offer schemes of work for the early years (see samples in Appendix 1).

The books and documents share some characteristics in emphasising the need for children to acquire skills: emotional and social, physical and creative, and in thinking and communicating. The documents sometimes differ in the kind of approach recommended, the specified nature of learning goals and the age by which children should be expected to achieve these.

There are genuine concerns about the kinds of experiences offered to children in combination nursery/reception classes or reception/year 1 classes, which include children who are bound by National Curriculum requirements. Do we need to *'maintain the practice of teaching children through their play'* (Nutbrown, 1998: 58) or should early-years education be more tightly structured in *all* education establishments?

The debate and differences of opinion are good: they heighten social awareness of the educational needs of young children, which must generate ideas, public and political questions, and *research*. Most importantly, professionals working with young children must speak out so that our opinions are heard and valued. These opinions are based on expertise and experience of how young children learn. We let our children down if we are not vocal on their behalf.

Good-quality learning environments

Examples of appropriate environments to stimulate science in the early years have been given throughout this book and a list of useful resources is given in Appendix 2. However, some necessary conditions are worth reiterating, regardless of the teaching approach adopted.

Space

Young children need *space*. There are Government guidelines on minimum space requirements although it can be difficult to adhere to these if the nursery or mainstream classroom is housed in an old, inappropriate building. Young children are physical: they need to move and develop their coordination and motor skills throughout the day. Areas designated for different types of play and first-hand experiences are essential throughout the foundation years of 3–6. Children need space for water- and sand-play, role-play, creative expression and construction, and *focused* cognitive development (e.g. science-based stimuli, mathematics, language). Young children need space for 'time-out', and, of course, outdoor-play.

Early-years buildings also need space for parents, guardians and other visitors. Good lobby areas adjacent to the nursery or classroom give space for pushchairs and strollers, for grandparents and toddlers to wait while brothers and sisters are collected, or brief but significant discussions to take place with the nursery nurse or class teacher. Lobbies provide space for displays of children's work or interesting artefacts. Additional parents' and/or project rooms will encourage support for school events and provide space for quiet withdrawal (adults and children) and parent groups. Space like this within the building integrates significant adults into the teaching and learning environment and habits of adult support for the carers and educators can be established at this stage.

Resources

Young children need good resources, although these are rarely budgeted for realistically. Access to good resources is particularly important for children coming from underprivileged backgrounds (according to the PPA, 800,000 5-year olds were at or below the poverty line in 1998).

However, good, safe toys cost money. Large or table-top hand lenses cost more than 3 cm diameter lenses, more appropriate for key stage 2 children. Young children need *binocular* microscopes as they are less adept at managing to close one eye to view objects through single-lens microscopes. Young children need access to first-class electricity kits: their motor skills are

Early-years education is not simply about keeping children quiet until we can *'deliver them to the next stage equipped to cause minimum disruption'* (Craig, 1996)

less accomplished than older children who can handle bare wire ends, and they need circuits that work *straight away*.

Young children learn through practical experiences more than reading for information, although there are now good non-fiction books and software available, as well as stories with a scientific story line (see Appendix). Unfortunately, even secondary sources for 3–6 years-olds are usually expensive. Young children's books are heavily illustrated, which raises the cost. 'Big Books' complement and reinforce individual readers but are costly.

Budgeting for resources should reflect the importance of young children's needs.

Time

Young children need time. This has been emphasised throughout this book: any young child's day, whether informal or structured, must include time to *play*, explore, visit and revisit materials or phenomena that will stimulate, raise questions and reinforce ideas and self-confidence.

It often seems that there are never enough hours in the day to accomplish our objectives but we can achieve more by involving children in the choice. They will become independent learners if we adopt approaches that encourage children to choose from within a range of good-quality experiences. The choosing teaches them to make decisions, keep to a schedule or sequence of activities, develop patience and take turns when play areas are at capacity.

Partnerships

This section begins by *praising* early-years educators. I have had the privilege of working with a wide range of staff responsible for the care and education of young children. I use the term 'staff' to include qualified teachers, whether nursery or key stage 1, nursery nurses, specialist teacher assistants and other specialist staff (SEN, etc.). Children receive the best possible education when the staff are well trained and operate as a team. Go into almost any early-years environment and you will see adults working positively and collaboratively. The team spirit is there but the training lags behind (Ghouri, 1999).

Of course, parents and guardians are integral to the success of young children's learning. Interested and supportive governing bodies enable the teaching and caring staff to achieve even more, and the enthusiasm, and sometimes tolerance, of the local community creates a positive environment for more expansive projects to take place (open days, fundraising, use of the school as a community meeting place).

Parents

Parents nowadays have less access to an extended family than 50 years ago and this means fewer role-models of older, effective parents. Parenting and early-years education is often undervalued. The late Joan Lestor MP suggested that we spend far more time learning to drive a car than we do learning to be parents. The school can offer a support system for those parents who are still discovering the joys and difficulties of raising children. I would not wish to be unrealistic. Both as a parent and as a teacher, I have attended evening events where, say, eight parents turned up out of a possible 240! Nevertheless, allocating space as advocated earlier, and regular after-school chats are ways of keeping parents informed and encouraging participation in topics or projects. Also, regular 'letters home' about current focuses, requests for information or artefacts, allow parents, whose full-time employment or other commitments prohibit daily/weekly contact, to be involved in their children's early education (see Chapter 8).

Reflective practice and professional development

All good schools, nurseries and playgroups allocate time on a frequent and regular basis for general discussion, planning and reflecting. In such meetings, ongoing programmes can be evaluated and adjusted, individual children's needs discussed and short-term action planned. Indeed as Dunlop (1998: 48) states:

It is apparent that the single most effective means of determining the success of pre-school and primary education, is the reflectiveness of the staff involved.

Such reflective practice needs to be consciously put into effect in the nursery or classroom. We take it for granted that we notice what is happening in the classroom, at a group or individual level. We note needs and interests and plan and implement appropriate responses. Sometimes we tell colleagues or parents about this. However, we are not in the habit of writing this down, partly because of time constraints and partly because of the wealth of information and changes that take place in a very short time.

We need to plan for internal professional development whereby time is allocated for staff to observe their own children without interruption (or at least not too much):

Action research, such as observing children for periods of time without intervention, has been successful in the professional development of early-years practitioners. Staff begin to focus on some aspect of learning, rather than assessing 'the children'. (Blenkin and Hutchin, 1998: 62)

Such strategies enable us to notice significant behaviour and discussions that the hurly burly of the teaching day denies. This can help us to plan appropriate provision for effective learning.

Over and beyond this, staff need opportunities for more in-depth analyses and in-service training. This is not readily available. Expansion of emphasis on early-years education and increased access for nursery/playgroup *'provision has not been accompanied by comparable development in training ... The majority of teachers working with the under fives are not qualified to work with such young children'* (Pugh, 1998: 13).

Furthermore, there are still far too few science specialists with early-years training so, for some time, it will be necessary for early-years educators to seek ideas from science specialists and/or early-years specialists and modify the advice accordingly. With the growing expertise overall, we will eventually have a body of experts who serve both areas well.

However, there are now more training opportunities for early-years educators:

- Courses for Specialist Teaching Assistants (STA).
- Degrees in Early Childhood Studies for teaching and non-teaching staff (BA.ECS).
- INSET on early childhood education provided by local universities and education authorities.
- Membership of national, focused groups, such as the National Association for Nursery Nurses (NANN); the Association for Science Education (ASE), with growing membership in the early years, free meetings and journals; the Professional Association of Early Childhood Educators; the British Association for Early Childhood Education (BAECE).

Influencing policy

The early years of children's lives are critical in terms of all aspects of their development. (Abbott and Pugh, 1998)

It is no longer enough for us to stay silent and simply react to demands made by well-intentioned but uninformed outsiders, whatever their status, or to respond to a 'top-down' philosophy. Early-years education is not simply about keeping children quiet until we can *'deliver them to the next stage equipped to cause minimum disruption'* (Craig, 1996), nor is it about preparing children to pass 'baseline assessment' although we have to be conscious of the criteria for this.

We have been, and continue to be, trained in how young children learn and the most appropriate environments and approaches for effective teaching in the early years. We need to inform colleagues and others about the differences and special provision that young children need. That means representing early-years education in local, regional and national committees. We have to be proactive and vocal if we are to make sure that our children have the best education that we can give them.

Let the children have the last word. Alison, an early-years educator, sees a child playing at the water-tray in the nursery:

Alison: *How many of those cups do you need to fill up your pail?*

Child: *I've got a cat.*

Alison: *How is the water getting into the sieve?*

Child: *His name is Ben.*

Alison: *What could you do to stop the water getting through the sieve?*

Child: *He hates fireworks.*

At this point Alison gives up and begins to walk away.

Child: *Hoy, Mrs!*

Alison: *Yes?*

Child: *10 of them ... through the holes ... use a paper towel.*

(Bishop and Whitfield, 1999)

Max de Bóo has spent many years working with young children, as a carer, a nursery teacher and in mainstream education, particularly at key stage 1. She has worked as an advisory teacher for science, supporting educators from early years to year 6. Max is currently a senior lecturer in education at the University of Hertfordshire, specialising in science and early-years education. She has written widely on these subjects and acts as a consultant and in-service training provider at a national level. Her interests and research have focused on young children's scientific thinking, language and science, and student-teachers' scientific background.

SCIENCE 3–6

Schemes of work for the early years

The following examples are pages taken from Local Education Authority schemes of work. They are included to show how much excellent material is available to early-years educators, almost always designed and tested by local teachers under the guidance of science advisers and advisory teachers and therefore likely to have particular relevance for children in that area. Adopting a local scheme means that there is access to local staff in early-years settings who have implemented the scheme already and who can share ideas and extensions to the material. The sample pages included vary in the amount of detail shown on the page but these, and most local schemes of work, describe the learning purposes, resources needed, strategies to help children achieve the objectives, time needed, vocabulary, cross-curricular links, and ideas for assessment, continuity and progression.

The samples have been chosen to show the similarity of purpose in local schemes of work, that is, they adopt a more holistic approach to learning in the early years and use a teaching approach based on practical first-hand experience in science. These samples have also been chosen because they illustrate the individuality of local schemes, variety that we should celebrate as evidence of the continued creativity of educators. The individuality also shows how objectives may be realised in different ways; local 'ownership' of planning documents has a positive and productive impact on the realisation of those objectives.

As with any scheme of work, it is always necessary to be thoroughly critical and compare local schemes with non-statutory, national schemes, whether produced by QCA (DfEE) or commercial suppliers. Early-years educators may choose to keep more than one publication for reference purposes.

The ASE is grateful to the following Local Education Authorities for permission to reproduce these extracts: Barking and Dagenham, Devon, Dorset, Hertfordshire, Newport, Fife.

Science in the Early Years

Year - Reception   **Area of Learning** - Knowledge and Understanding of the World   **Time scale** - 4 weeks

Focus - Living Things and the Environment - Other Animals

Learning Intention - To recognise, and know the names of, a variety of animals

To develop an awareness of where different animals live

Learning Objectives (to include Knowledge and Understanding, Skills and Attitudes)	Teaching		Resource Provision	Specific Vocabulary to be Developed
	Strategy	Adult Role		
To sort farm animals in various ways: - by number of legs - by colour - by type	Arrange a visit to a farm and/or mobile farm to visit nursery.	Model a way of sorting and explain it to the children. Questioning - "Can you find another way to sort the animals?", etc.	Sets of toy farm animals of varying sizes and colours	colour names animal names cow, pig, horse, sheep, goat, chicken, etc.
To make simple direct comparisons.	Sort farm animals into sets by size.	Questioning - "Which is the biggest/smallest?", etc.		same, different, big, little
To describe farm animals from direct observations.	Provide toy animals for the children to describe and talk about with each other.	Questioning - "What can you tell me about your animal?", "Can you tell me something else?", etc.	Sets of toy farm animals of varying sizes and colours	same, different animal names colour names big, little
To identify farm animals from descriptions.	Provide a hat with a picture of a farm animal on it. Children must give information so that the child wearing the hat can guess the animal.	Modelling descriptions of the animals. Use questioning to support and guide the children that are giving clues.	Hat. Pictures of farm animals.	same, different animal names colour names big, little
To begin to ask questions to find out information.	Hide an animal in a bag and ask the children to ask questions to find out what it is.	Model questions to support and guide the children.	Feely bag. Toy farm animals.	same, different animal names colour names big, little
To know the names of farm animals and their young.	Free play with toy farm animals and their young.	Teacher interaction to support the children's play.	Sets of toy farm animals including adults and young.	cow - calf horse - foal chicken - chick sheep - lamb pig - piglet goat - kid
	Play 'animals and their young' picture matching game.	Model the language of adult and young, then give the children the opportunity to use it themselves.	'Animals and their young' picture matching game.	

Repeat for other groups of animals, e.g. pets, zoo animals. Emphasis where we would find the different types of animal, e.g. home, zoo, jungle, etc.

1– MOVEMENT

"DO" K&U of the world, Creative development, physical development
Sc2 Humans, Sc3 Materials, Sc4 Forces and motion

1 How many ways can you move across the floor?

Purpose: To think of using a range of body parts to facilitate movement .

Resources: Themselves.

Activities: In a large space, to think for themselves and to consider how many different ways they can move, then how many ways can they skip, and finally jump.
Ask them to demonstrate new ways to each other, and try to copy their friends' style.
They can hold long streamers, or have a large card disc taped to the part of the body that is leading or a focus of the movement.

2 How do clockwork toys move?

Purpose: To identify how energy is given to the toys and what happens.

Resources: Clockwork toys.

Activities: Let children play with a variety of toys, to watch how they move, and to put them into sets.
Ask children to work in pairs and to choose a toy. They can mime what happens, with one putting in the energy and one being the toy.

3 Make a number spinner and have a game.

Purpose: To introduce gravity and spinners.

Resources: Mathematical spinners, card discs and doweling.

Activities: Show children how to use spinners used for maths games. Provide a range of different size discs for them to make their own spinners. Ask them to devise a game to play with a friend.

4 Roll a car down a ramp to hit a target.

Purpose: To observe that cars need to be pushed to make them move and that the speed can be altered by the angle of the slope.

Resources: Toy cars, wooden plank, target.

Activities: Let the children explore what happens when toy cars are allowed to roll down slopes of different heights. Ask them to notice how far the car goes and where. Encourage them to make a game to see if they can hit a target.

15 Can you make a domino snake?

Purpose: To develop the concepts of forces and movement.

Resources: Sets of dominoes.

Activities: Ask groups of children to use dominoes and to discover how many different ways they can stand they to create interesting patterns of movement.
The ideas of each group can be put together to create a domino run using chain reactions.

16 Make a see-saw for teddy bears.

Purpose: To introduce the concept of balance.

Resources: Construction kits or building blocks.

Activities: Challenge the children to make a see-saw on which 2 teddy bears can balance.
What happens if the bears are of unequal size?

17 Try rolling and bouncing balls. Which bounces the best?

Purpose: To observe the movements of, and to appreciate that, the properties of materials make them react in different ways.

Resources: Selection of large and small balls, all possible shapes and materials.

Activities: Use different balls and talk about the differences.
Let them discover how balls behave when dropped from different heights and on to different surfaces.

18 Roll a marble through a tube fast and slow.

Purpose: To observe that different slopes and materials can influence the speed of a moving object.

Resources: Marbles, tubes and boxes etc.

Activities: Give children the opportunity to play with a set of different lengths of tube,marbles, table tennis balls, polystyrene balls, and other spheres.
If possible show them a manufactured marble run game. Challenge them to make a marble run.

EARLY YEARS SCHEME OF WORK

Unit G. LIGHT and COLOUR

Prior experiences that may have contributed to their current understanding	What do we want them to learn	How to find out their current understanding	Classroom experiences to help them understand better		Yes! This tells us that they have understood it
			Type	Activity	
Light Sunshine, bedside light, torch, birthday candles, Christmas tree lights, Divali, photo flash, street lights, bonfire night, fireworks, car lights, T.V..., computer, in the fridge, night lights, spots of light reflected off shiny surfaces (mirrors), onto the wall/ceiling etc. Darkness, the moon, stars, trainers that flash when you walk. Shiny surfaces, traffic lights, crossing lights, green flashing man. Objects make shadows in the sun.	**Reception** There are different sources of light.	How do I make it light?	Sort	Show and tell - children bring in variety of toys/pictures/things that give off light	They say that sun, torch, fire etc give off light
	There is light and dark.	What happens if we turn off the light and draw the curtains?	Research	Read about animals that live underground moles, foxes, worms, badgers etc. 'Owl babies', 'The Owl Who Was Afraid of the Dark', 'Can't you Sleep Little Bear?'	They know that owls and other animals prefer to live in the dark.
Colour Toys, clothes, pictures, wallpaper, television, (the environment), traffic, picture books, painting, talk about colours, use coloured pencils and crayons, favourite colours - "I can sing a rainbow"	The names of colours. (see Vocab)	Quiz: name the colours.	Observe	Colour dominoes. Song 'Who's wearing blue today .....?' (children participate)	They know that mixing 2 colours makes a different colour.
	Vocab: light, dark, red, blue, green, yellow.		Sort	Sort by colour (including different tones) Matching a colour card to objects in the environment.	
	Mixing can make new colours. Colours can be dark and light shades.	How can we get different colours?	Explore	Mixing paint, modelling clay. Tie dyeing	They show how blue and yellow make green and how pink can be made by adding red to white.
	Year 1 There are many things that can give off light.	Ask "Where does light come from?" and collect ideas.	Survey	Make a collection (list or pictures) of where light comes from. Make a circuit with a bulb.	They can draw or list torch, candle, room light, fire, fireworks, sun etc.
	Darkness is the absence of light.	How do I make it dark?	Observe	Where is the darkest place in the school, at home? What makes it so dark there? Cover a table with thick overhanging material - use torches to light it.	They say that it is dark where there is no light.
	Shadows are formed where the light is blocked.	Draw yourself with your shadow	Explore	Silhouettes of children's heads. Shadow games in the playground. Shine light at/through objects.	They know that shadows are produced because the light is blocked out.
	Names and combinations of primary colours	Presented with primary colours - what colour can you make?	Explore	Mix primary colours.	They say that mixing colours changes them. They can make green, orange, purple and brown.
	Colours of the rainbow.	What are the colours of the rainbow?	Observe Research	Paint/draw a rainbow. Find pictures of rainbows. Are the colours in the pictures the same as a real rainbow?	They know the colours of the rainbow

earlysow

Nursery – Fairy Tales

Detailed Topic Activities

General Learning Objective: to look at the world about them based on ideas from stories
Activities will obviously be dependent on the tales selected. The following are just a few possible examples.

First hand

Cinderella — observe a pumpkin; make lanterns; try on shoes - find the shoe that fits; keep some white mice (from reputable source); role play dressing for a ball/different occasions

Sleeping Beauty — look in mirrors including concave and convex; spin some wool

Billy Goat Gruff — visit a farm to see goats; build bridges; role play crossing the bridge

Puss in Boots — bring in a cat; how do you look after cats/what do cats need

second hand

look at pictures/videos of the animals or situations concerned; consult non-fiction books; paint/collage something from the story

close observation

use a magnifier to look at the pumpkin; look at yourself in other shiny things - how good are they as a mirror? What can you see? listen to the sound of a cat; listen to other animal sounds - can you guess the animal?

collections

other large vegetables; different vehicles and carriages eg royal processions shiny objects; pictures of different bridges cats - pictures, toy, ornaments, artefacts with illustrations, other famous cats - Garfield, Tom etc.

matching/sequencing

simple stages of the story; pattern with shoe prints; simple weaving pattern

special equipment

magnifiers; tape recorder; assorted mirrors

ongoing

sand — moving vehicles/toy animals through sand - can you see where they have been? Footprints in sand

water — cleaning things; making rivers under bridges

construction — building vehicles, building bridges - how strong are they?

food technology — preparing and cooking pumpkin and other vegetables; making animal shaped biscuits

DETECTIVES - TOPIC 6
SCIENCE - NURSERY /RECEPTION

General Learning Objectives	To explore their world using appropriate senses. To use their senses to make observations.	
Working towards	Sc1 2a, 2b, Sc1 3c	

	NURSERY	RECEPTION
Key Experiences	Scientific activities to deliver key experiences	Progression in activities
Direct Experiences	Talk about parts of the body where senses are situated and what they do. Provide materials for testing, smelling, hearing, touching and seeing games. How we use our senses to gain information about our world. Making instruments that have different sounds. Use of feely bags to describe objects. Cookery sessions to use all senses especially smell and taste. Listening / sensory walks.	Collection of textures. Feeling around blindfold. Looking at objects through the eye, magnifying glass (microscope) Use of feely bags / boxes (use light box in things to try section). Close observations. Listening skills - can we hear a pin drop ? Familiar smells. NB: See safety note on foods. Cover all five senses.
Supplementary Experiences	Listening tapes sound discrimination. Sound lotto.	Communication - deaf language. How we pass information on to others. Body language visits from Hearing / Visually Impaired Unit (Margaret Barrell / Ann Kelly). Listening tapes, sound discrimination. Sound Lotto. Fourways farm (Channel 4). Techniquest visit.
Investigational skills and on-going structured activities	Discuss likes and dislikes of sound, taste, smell, feel and appearance. Introduce new vocabulary of senses and descriptions of soft, rough, smooth. What plants can be found outside - are they the same ? What are the differences.	Do foods taste the same if we can't see / smell them (blindfold and hold nose). Cover what is visible containers. Match smells to pictures - cheese / coffee etc. Guess the instrument (beyond a screen).

SCIENCE - NURSERY /RECEPTION

General Learning Objectives		
Working towards		

	NURSERY	RECEPTION
Key Experiences	Scientific activities to deliver key experiences	Progression in activities
Outstanding Skills	What do you see ? What can you see ? What can you hear ? How does it feel ? What you can smell ? What does it taste like ?	What can you say with your eyes ? What can you say with your hands ? What smells do you like / dislike ?
Sorting and Sequencing	Likes / dislikes of all five senses. Different textures / sounds. Sequencing sounds soft to loud. Touch, soft to hard. Sight, Dark to light. Sorting and matching group features (1 sort)	Pictograms of favourite food / smell. Sorting and matching group features (2 sorts)
Resources	Clue books: Allen and Denslow. Science Wise Parker and Ward, Nelson. Bearhunt: Pam Adams. Walk in the Park: Anthony B. Rosie's Walk: Pat Hutchings I thought I: Pam Adams	Foods / Food stuff materials for touch. Photograph feely bag. Magnifying classes, musical instruments, blind folds.

© Fife Council Education Service (Scottish curriculum)

STUDY DESCRIPTION

ENVIRONMENTAL STUDIES 5-14

TITLE Toys	MAIN COMPONENT Science	P1 - P3

Key Features	Suggested Activities	Skills
KU Sc 6 - Forces and their effects Sc 6a, 6b, 6c	**Moving toys** - finding out what happens when toys are pushed and pulled - recording and reporting that forces change movement of objects eg make stationary objects move, stop moving objects, change direction of movement - challenging groups to find out as many ways as possible to move a toy. Presenting their ideas to the class - finding out that toys need an energy source to move - battery, clockwork (spring), being pushed - grouping toys according to their energy source for movement - investigating sliding objects on slopes with different surfaces to introduce idea of frictional force.	C 2, 6 R 1 C 2 R 1, 2 E 1 C 2 C 1 C 1, 6 E 3
Sc 6 - Forces and their effects Sc 6d	• **Pivots and Wheels** - finding out what happens when a force is applied to objects around a pivot eg model figure with moving arms, legs, door, see-saw - presenting this information to the class.	C 2, 6 R 2
Sc 6 - Forces and their effects Sc 6a	• **Floating and Sinking** - predicting which objects from a selection will float and which will sink - testing their prediction and presenting their information - finding out how to sink floaters and how to float sinkers	P 4 C 2, 6 R 1, 2 C 6
T 8 - Properties of materials and tools in relation to their practical uses T 8a	• Looking at different kinds of materials used to make toys and their effectiveness - plastic, wood, metal, fabric.	C 10 E 10
T 1 - Technology and human needs H 2 - Relationships T 1a H 2b, 2c	• Discussing why we need toys - sharing feelings about a favourite toy. - learning to look after and share classroom toys - tidying up routines.	E 10, 12 H 2 P 21 H 2 P 21 H 3
T 5 - Technology responding to values and scientific progress T 5a	• Researching how toys have changed by looking at photographs, books, real examples.	P 18 C 10 E 12
SS 8 - Developing an understanding of the nature of historical evidence. SS 8a SS 9 - Considering the meaning of heritage SS 9a	• Possible activities for Design and Make I - design and make a simple wheeled vehicle - design and make a card figure with moving parts.	

Identify opportunities for collection of samples of pupils' work for assessment.

Jan 95

Appendix 2

SCIENCE 3–6

Some basic resources for early-years science enquiries

B = Borrow; C = Collect; M = Make;
P = Purchase

Aluminium/kitchen foil	*P*
Aquaria/water tanks	*P*
Balances/bathroom scales	*P*
Balloons	*P*
Balls, various	C/P
Batteries for electricity kit	*P*
Beans, various, dried	*P*
Bells, various	C/P
Bicycle, occasionally	*B*
Bird table and bird food	P/M
Bones, hygienic, dry	C
Blotting paper/nappies	*P*
Breads, fresh (explore)	*P*
Bubble solution	M
Bulbs and buzzers (electricity kit)	*P*
Building blocks	*P*
Camera	*B*
Candles	C/P
Cars, toys	C/P
Charcoals	C/P
Colour filters	*P*

Coloured materials	C
Construction kits/toys	*P*
Cooking utensils	*P*
Cotton reels	C/P
Cotton thread/string	C/P
Cotton wool	*P*
Dolls, small and large, different ethnic ones	C/P
Electricity kits, suitable	*P*
Eye droppers/pipettes	*P*
Fabrics, various	C
Fans, various	C
Feathers (care/asthma)	C
Filter papers/coffee filters	*P*
Fishing nets	*P*
Floaters and sinkers	C
Flowers for exploration	C/P
Flower press	*P*
Foods and fruits, fresh and dried (explore/cook)	C/P
Food colourings	*P*
Funnels	*P*
Garden tools, suitable	*P*
Hair dryer	*P*
Hand lenses, plastic	*P*

Herbs (indoor garden)	M/P
Horn (old car one)	B
Household ingredients, e.g. vinegar, salt, flour, sugar, cornflour	C/P
Insect viewers	C/P
Jars, plastic (and glass if school policy allows)	C/P
Jelly moulds	B/P
Kaleidoscopes	B/P
Lenses	P
Magnets	P
Magnifiers, table-top	P
Maps or games, simple	P
Matches (kept safely)	P
Materials, various	C
Measuring equipment	P
Mechanical toys	P
Metals, various, including coins	C/P
Microscopes	P
Minibeasts, dead (safe) and alive (temporary)	C
Mirrors, plastic, plane and curved	P
Motors (electricity kits)	P
Musical instruments and sound makers	M/P
Nesting box	M
Paper, varieties of	P
Pastas, various	P
Petri dishes or saucers	C/P
Plaster of Paris	P
Plastic bags, supermarket	C
Pooters	P
Pots, various	C
Prisms	P
Pumps, water, balloon, bicycle	C/P
Ramps	M

Recycled materials	C
Rocks and fossils	C/P
Salt	P
Sand	P
Sand/glass-paper	P
Sand-timers and stopclocks	P
Saucepans	P
Seeds and seedsprouters	P
Shells	C
Sieves	C/P
Squeezy bottles	C
Stethoscope (real/toy)	P
Straws	P
Switches (electricity kit)	P
Syringes, plastic	P
Thermometers, including liquid crystal	P
Toys, including moving parts	P
Tubing, plastic	P
Tuning forks	P
Vegetables, fresh for exploration and cooking	P
Vegetable oil	P
Washing-up liquid to make bubble solution	P
Water clocks	M
Water tanks, transparent	P
Water wheels	P
Wind gauge, simple	M/P
Wood, different types	C/P
Woodwork tools	P
Wormery	M/P
Yoghurt pots, etc.	C

For further information and advice on appropriate types of equipment and its safe use, see the ASE book *Primary science equipment* by Rosemary Feasey (ASE, 1998).

Appendix 3

Appropriate software resources

Title (for Mac and PC unless specified)	Age range (5–7+ unless specified)	Supplier
Encyclopedia of science		Dorling Kindersley
Encyclopedia of space and the universe		Dorling Kindersley
First look series	2.5 - 4	Inclusive Technology
How things work		Dorling Kindersley
Living and growing CD-ROM		Inclusive Technology
My first amazing dictionary		Dorling Kindersley
Nature		Dorling Kindersley
Ozzie otter		Softkeys
Primary ClipArt CD-ROM	6+	
Sammy's science house (PC only)	4+	Edmark
My world scenarios (Mac only)		Hyperstudio
Botanical garden – sunburst		Hyperstudio
Mouse practice		Hyperstudio

List collated by Geoff Strack
Consultant for ICT and Science

References

Abbott, L. and Pugh, G. (1998) *Training to work in the early years: developing the climbing frame.* Buckingham: Open University Press.

Anning, A. (1994) Play and the legislated curriculum. Back to basics: an alternative view. In *The excellence of play*, ed. Moyles, J. R. Buckingham: Open University Press.

ASE (1991) *School home investigations in primary science (SHIPS) infants pack.* Hatfield: Association for Science Education.

Athey, C. (1990) *Extending thought in young children: a parent–teacher relationship.* London: Paul Chapman.

Barnes, D. (1976) *From communication to curriculum.* Harmondsworth: Penguin.

Bearne, E. ed. (1998) *Use of language across the primary curriculum.* London: Routledge.

Bishop, A. and Whitfield, P. (1999) Supporting children's scientific and mathematical development through play in the nursery. In *The challenge of change: Report of the 4th summer conference for teacher education in primary science.* School of Education, Durham University.

Blenkin, G. and Kelly, A. V. (1996) *Early childhood education: a developmental curriculum.* London: Paul Chapman.

Blenkin, G. and Hutchin, V. (1998) Action research child observations and professional development: some evidence from a research project. *Early Years,* **19**(1), 62–75.

Brown, A. L., Campione, J. C., Metz, K. E. and Ash, D. B. (1997) The development of science learning abilities in children. In *Growing up with science: developing early understanding of science,* ed. Härnquist, K. and Burgen, A. London: Jessica Kingsley Publishers.

Bruce, T. (1992) Preface. In *Exploring learning: young children and block play,* ed. Gura, P. London: Paul Chapman.

Bruner, J. S., Olver, R. R. and Greenfield, P. M. (1966) *Studies in cognitive growth.* Wiley: New York.

Bruner, J. (1980) *Under five in Britain* (Oxford Pre-School Research Project 1). London: Grant McIntyre.

Bruner, J. (1996) What we have learned about early learning. *European Early Childhood Education Research Journal,* **4**(1), 5–16.

Carey, S. (1985) *Conceptual change in childhood.* Cambridge MA: Massachusetts Institute of Technology Press.

Carter, R. ed. (1991) *Knowledge about language and the curriculum: the LINC Reader.* London: Hodder and Stoughton.

Craig, P. (1996) Talk at the Annual Meeting of the Association for Science Education (ASE).

David, T. (1996) Curriculum in the early years. In *Contemporary issues in the early years: working collaboratively for children,* ed. Pugh, G. 2nd edn. London: Paul Chapman/National Children's Bureau.

Dean, J. (1992) 2nd edn. *Organising learning in the primary classroom.* London: Routledge.

de Bóo, M. (1985) Child-centred studies. *Education in Science,* **113**, 19–21.

de Bóo, M. (1999) *Enquiring children, challenging teaching: investigating science processes.* Buckingham: Open University Press.

DES (1985) *Education for all (The Swann Report).* London: HMSO.

DES (1989) *The Education Reform Act. Circular 5/89.* London: Department of Education and Science.

Desforges, C. (1993) *Children as thinkers and as learners.* London: BAECE (British Association for Early Childhood Education).

Desforges C. W. ed. (1989) Early childhood education. *The British Journal of Educational Psychology,* Monograph series no. 4. Edinburgh: Scottish Academic Press.

DES/WO (1987) *National Curriculum Science Working Group: Interim Report.* London: Department of Education and Science.

DES/WO (1989) *Science in the National Curriculum.* London: HMSO.

DES/WO (1991) *Science in the National Curriculum.* London: HMSO.

DFE (1995) *Science in the National Curriculum.* London: HMSO.

DfEE (1997) *Desirable outcomes for children's learning on entering compulsory education.* London: The Stationery Office.

DfEE (1998) *Circular 4/98. Teaching: high status, high standards. Requirements for courses of initial teacher training.* London: Department for Education and Employment.

DfEE (1999) Early learning goals. London: The Stationery Office.

Donaldson, M. (1978) *Children's minds.* Glasgow: Fontana.

Driver, R., Leach, J., Millar, R. and Scott, P. (1996) *Young people's images of science.* Buckingham: Open University Press.

Dunlop, A. W. (1998) Assessment as part of a continuity study. *Early Years,* **19**(1), 39–49.

EYTARN (1999) *Planning for excellence.* London (77 Holloway Road, N4 8JZ): Early Years Teachers Anti-Racist Network.

Feasey, R. (1999) *Primary science and literacy.* Hatfield, Herts: Association for Science Education.

Gallas, K. (1995) *Talking their way into science.* New York: Teachers' College Press.

Ghouri, N. (1999) Early-years foundation will 'flop'. *Times Educational Supplement,* 2 April, p.10.

Goldish, M. (1996) *101 Science poems and songs for young learners.* New York: Scholastic.

Hall, S. (1992) Race, culture and communications: looking backward and forward in cultural studies. *Rethinking Marxism,* **5**.

Harding, S. ed. (1993) *The 'racial' economy of science.* Indiana University Press.

Harlen, W. (1983) *Guides to assessment in education: Science.* London: Macmillan/Nelson.

Harlen, W. and Jelly, S. (1992) *Developing science in the primary classroom.* Edinburgh: Oliver and Boyd.

Harlen, W. (1996) 2nd edn. *The teaching of science in primary schools.* London: David Fulton.

Harris, D. B. (1985) *Goodenough-Harris drawing test.* NY: Harcourt, Brace & World Inc.

Hayton, M. (1995) Thinking it through: young children thinking science. In *Science with reason,* ed. Atkinson, A. and Fleer, M. London: Hodder and Stoughton.

Hodson, D. (1998) Personalizing, de-mythologising and politicizing: critical multiculturalism in science and technology education. In *Critical multiculturalism: rethinking multicultural and antiracist education,* ed. May, S. London: Routledge.

Holt, J. (1965) *How children fail.* London: Pitman.

Hughes, M. (1986) *Children and number.* Oxford: Basil Blackwell.

Hurst, V. (1997) *Planning for early learning.* London: Paul Chapman.

Isaacs, N. (1974) *Children's ways of knowing.* New York: Teachers' College Press.

Johnston, J. (1992) The science strait-jacket. *Primary Science Review,* **25**, 8–9.

Johnston, J. (1996) *Early explorations in science.* Buckingham: Open University Press.

Johnston, J. (1998) Learning science in the early years. In *ASE guide to primary science education,* ed. Sherrington, R. pp. 76–82. Cheltenham: Stanley Thornes.

Johnston, J. and Gray, A. (1999) *Enriching early scientific learning.* Buckingham: Open University Press.

Katz, L. G. (1977) *Talks with teachers.* Washington: NAEYC.

Katz, L. G. (1995) *Talks with teachers of young children.* London: Ablex.

Kelly, A. (1985) The construction of masculine science. *British Journal of Sociology of Education,* **6**, 133–154.

Kenway, J., Blackmore, J., Willis, S. and Rennie, L. (1996) The emotional dimensions of feminist pedagogy in schools. In *Equity in the classroom: towards effective pedagogy for girls and boys,* ed. Murphy, P. and Gipps, C. London: UNESCO/Falmer Press.

Keogh, B. and Naylor, S. (1997) *Thinking about science.* Sandbach, Cheshire: Millgate House Publishers.

Lane, J. (1999) With equal concern... *Child Education,* **76**(6), 45–47.

Lansdown, G. (1996) Respecting the right of children to be heard. In *Contemporary issues in the early years: working collaboratively for children,* ed. Pugh, G. 2nd edn. London: Paul Chapman/National Children's Bureau.

MacLeod-Brudenell, I. (1998) *The design and technology handbook for pre-school providers.* London: The Design and Technology Association.

Mathews, J. (1996) The young child's representation and drawing. In *Early childhood education: a developmental curriculum,* ed. Blenkin, G. and Kelly, A. V. London: Paul Chapman.

Merry, R. (1998) *Successful children, successful teaching.* Buckingham: Open University Press.

Millar, R., Gott, R., Lubben, F. and Duggan, S. (1995) Children's performance of investigative tasks in science: a framework for considering progression. In *Progression in learning,* BERA Dialogues 11, ed. Hughes, M. pp, 82–108. Clevedon, Bristol: Multilingual Matters.

Mitchell, C. and Koshy, V. (1995) 2nd edn. *Effective teacher assessment: looking at children's learning in the primary classroom.* London: Hodder and Stoughton.

Moyles, J. R. (1989) *Just playing? The role and status of play in early childhood education.* Buckingham: Open University Press.

Moyles, J. R. (1994) *The excellence of play.* Buckingham: Open University Press.

Munn, P. and Kleinberg, S. (1998) *A developmental framework for early literacy and numeracy.* University of Central Lancashire.

Murphy, P. and Gipps, C. ed. (1996) *Equity in the classroom: towards effective pedagogy for girls and boys.* London: UNESCO/Falmer Press.

Nuffield Primary Science (1995) *Nuffield Primary Science Teacher's guides.* London: Collins Educational.

Nutbrown, C. (1998) Early assessment – examining the baselines. *Early Years*, **19**(1), 50–61.

Outterside, Y. R. (1994) The emergence of scientific and technological awareness in the early years. In *The international conference on design and technology educational research and curriculum development.* Loughborough University.

Piaget, J. (1969) *Science of education and the psychology of the child.* London: Longman.

Pollard, A. (1997) The basics and eagerness to learn: a new curriculum for primary schooling. Mimeo. Graduate School of Education, University of Bristol.

Pre-school Playgroups Association (1991/2) *What children learn in playgroup; Science through play; Technology through play.* London (Freepost WC 5617, Croydon CR9 2WZ): PPA.

Pugh, G. (1998) Understand the under fives. *Times Educational Supplement*, 16 October, p.13.

QCA (1999) *The review of the desirable outcomes for children's learning on entering compulsory education.* London: Qualifications and Curriculum Authority.

Ratcliffe, M. (1998) The purposes of science education. In *ASE guide to primary science education*, ed. Sherrington, R. pp. 3–12. Cheltenham: Stanley Thornes.

Reiss, M. (1993) *Science education for a pluralist society.* Buckingham: Open University Press.

Roberts, R. (1998) Thinking about me and them: personal and social development. In *A curriculum development handbook for early childhood educators*, ed. Siraj-Blatchford, I. London: Trentham Books.

Ross, C. and Browne, N. (1993) *Girls as constructors in the early years.* London: Trentham Books.

SCAA (1997) *Looking at children's learning: desirable outcomes for children's learning on entering compulsory education.* London. School Curriculum and Assessment Authority.

Schools Council (1967–1974) *Science 5/13.* London: Macdonald Educational.

Science Processes and Concept Exploration (SPACE) (1990–98) Various reports. Liverpool: CRIPSAT, Liverpool University.

Sherrington, R. (1993) Science and language. In *ASE primary science teachers' handbook*, ed. Sherrington, R. pp. 196–206. Hemel Hempstead: Simon and Schuster.

Siraj-Blatchford, J. (1996) Learning science, technology and social justice: an integrated approach for 3 to 13 year olds. *Education Now*, **24**, 16–22.

Siraj-Blatchford, J. and MacLeod-Brudenell, I. (1999) *Supporting science, design and technology in the early years.* Buckingham: Open University Press.

Smith, P. K. and Cowie, H. (1991) *Understanding children's development.* Oxford: Blackwell.

SOED (1993) *Environmental Studies 5–14: National guidelines.* Edinburgh: Scottish Education Department.

Sparks Linfield, R. (1998) In the science corner. *Primary Science Review*, **54**, 24.

Sylva, K. (1986) *Monitoring the High Scope Training Programme.* London: Volcuf.

Sylva, K. (1994) The impact of early learning on children's later development. In *Start right: the importance of early learning.* London: Royal Society of Arts.

Thorpe, S., Deshpande, P. and Edwards, C. ed. (1994) *Race, equality and science teaching: a teachers' handbook.* Hatfield: Association for Science Education.

Tinbergen, N. (1976) *The importance of being playful.* London: BAECE (British Association for Early Childhood Education) Publications.

Tizard, B. and Hughes, M. (1984) *Young children learning: talking and thinking at home and at school.* London: Fontana.

Troyna, B. and Hatcher, R. (1991) *Racism in children's lives: a study of mainly-white primary schools.* London: NCB/Routledge.

Vygotsky, L. S. (1962) *Thought and language.* (Trans. Haufmann, E. and Vakar, G.) Cambridge, MA: Massachusetts Institute of Technology Press.

Vygotsky, L. S. (1978) *Mind in society.* Harvard University Press.

Wetton, N. and Cansell, P. (1993) *Feeling good: raising self-esteem in the primary school.* London: Forbes.

Wray, D. and Medwell, J. ed. (1994) *Teaching Primary English – the state of the art:* London Routledge.

Wright, C. (1992) Early education: multiracial primary school classrooms. In *Racism and education: structures and strategies*, ed. Gill, D., Mayor, B. and Blair, M. London: Sage.

4. When a current passes through a solution of lead(II) nitrate, 2.08 g of lead are deposited on the cathode. What volume of oxygen (at r.t.p.) is evolved at the anode?

5. A current passes through two cells in series. In the first, 0.300 mole of copper is deposited. In the second, 0.200 mole of chromium is deposited. Use this information to calculate the charge on the chromium ion.

6. Which of the following gives the number of moles of sodium atoms, zinc atoms and aluminium atoms which can be discharged by the passage of 96 500 coulombs of electricity?

   A 1 mole Na, 2 mole Zn, 3 mole Al

   B 1/96 500 mole Na, 2/96 500 mole Zn, 3/96 500 mole Al
   C 3 mole Na, 2 mole Zn, 1 mole Al
   D 1 mole Na, 1/2 mole Zn, 1/3 mole Al

Section 2

1. Which one of the following requires the largest quantity of electricity for discharge at an electrode?

   A 1 mole of Cr^{3+} ions

   B 2 moles of Pt^{2+} ions

   C 3 moles of Hg^{2+} ions

   D 4 moles of OH^- ions

   E 5 moles of Br^- ions

2. The Faraday constant is 96 500 C/mol, and $A_r(Cu) = 64$. Which of the following shows the mass of copper liberated at the cathode when a current of 0.10 ampere flows for 500 seconds through a solution of a copper(II) salt?

   A $\dfrac{64 \times 500 \times 0.10}{2 \times 96\,500}$ B $\dfrac{64 \times 96\,500}{2 \times 500 \times 0.10}$

   C $\dfrac{64 \times 96\,500}{500 \times 0.10}$ D $\dfrac{64 \times 500 \times 0.10}{96\,500 \times 60}$

3. A current of 0.200 ampere passes for 5.00 hours through a solution of gold ions. A mass of 2.45 g of gold ($A_r = 197$) is deposited on the cathode. Which of these expressions gives the charge on a gold ion?

   A $\dfrac{2.45 \times 0.200 \times 5.00 \times 60 \times 60}{197 \times 96\,500}$

   B $\dfrac{0.200 \times 5.00 \times 60 \times 60 \times 197}{96\,500 \times 2.45}$

   C $\dfrac{2.45 \times 96\,500}{197 \times 0.200 \times 5.00 \times 60 \times 60}$

   D $\dfrac{197 \times 0.200 \times 5.00 \times 60 \times 60 \times 96\,500}{2.45}$

4. Which of these expressions gives the mass of aluminium deposited when a current of 0.100 ampere flows for 6.00 minutes through molten alumina?

A $\dfrac{27 \times 6.00 \times 60 \times 0.100}{3 \times 96\,500}$ B $\dfrac{3 \times 6.00 \times 60 \times 0.100}{27 \times 96\,500}$

C $\dfrac{27 \times 6.00 \times 60 \times 0.100}{96\,500}$ D $\dfrac{27 \times 6.00 \times 60}{3 \times 96\,500 \times 0.100}$

5. When a current of 0.15 ampere flows for 4.0 hours, 0.71 g of copper is deposited on a cathode. Which expression gives the charge on a copper ion? ($A_r(Cu) = 64$)

A $\dfrac{0.15 \times 4.0 \times 60 \times 60 \times 64 \times 0.71}{96\,500}$

B $\dfrac{0.15 \times 4.0 \times 60 \times 60 \times 0.71}{64 \times 96\,500}$

C $\dfrac{64 \times 0.15 \times 4.0 \times 60 \times 60}{96\,500 \times 0.71}$ D $\dfrac{96\,500 \times 0.71}{0.15 \times 4.0 \times 60 \times 60 \times 64}$

6. A current of 0.10 ampere passes for 3.0 hours through a dilute solution of sulphuric acid. Which of the following represents the volume of oxygen (in dm^3 at r.t.p.) evolved at the anode?

A $\dfrac{0.10 \times 3.0 \times 60 \times 60 \times 4.0}{96\,500 \times 24}$ B $\dfrac{0.10 \times 3.0 \times 60 \times 60 \times 24}{96\,500 \times 4.0}$

C $\dfrac{0.10 \times 3.0 \times 60 \times 60 \times 24}{96\,500}$ D $\dfrac{0.10 \times 3.0 \times 60 \times 60}{24 \times 96\,500 \times 4}$

Section 3

1. A current of 1.00 A passes for 96.5 hours through molten anhydrous calcium chloride. What mass of calcium is deposited?

2. A current of 0.0200 A passed for 2.50 hours through a solution of a salt of the metal M. The mass of M deposited on the cathode was 0.0349 g. The relative atomic mass of M is 56. What is the charge on the ions of M?

3. A silversmith has made a silver bracelet which he wants to plate with gold. He calculates that it will need a layer of gold of mass 1.00 g. He makes the bracelet the cathode in a solution of gold(III) nitrate and switches on a current of 2.00 mA. For how many hours will he need to run the current?

4. Chlorine is made by electrolysing a concentrated solution of sodium chloride. In a diaphragm cell a current of 60 000 amperes is used. In order to obtain $12 \times 10^3 \, dm^3$ (at r.t.p.) of chlorine, for how long (to the nearest minute) would the cell need to operate?

5. Copper is purified by an electrolytic method. Copper dissolves from an anode of impure copper and is deposited on a cathode of pure copper. A current of 250 A is passed through a cell for 14 days. What increase in mass of the cathode occurs?

Answers to Problems

Chapter 1

Practice with Equations

1.   (a) $H_2(g) + CuO(s) \rightarrow Cu(s) + H_2O(g)$
    (b) $C(s) + CO_2(g) \rightarrow 2CO(g)$
    (c) $C(s) + O_2(g) \rightarrow CO_2(g)$
    (d) $Mg(s) + H_2SO_4(aq)$
              $\rightarrow H_2(g) + MgSO_4(aq)$
    (e) $Cu(s) + Cl_2(g) \rightarrow CuCl_2(s)$
2.   (a) $Ca(s) + 2H_2O(l)$
              $\rightarrow H_2(g) + Ca(OH)_2(aq)$
    (b) $2Cu(s) + O_2(g) \rightarrow 2CuO(s)$
    (c) $4Na(s) + O_2(g) \rightarrow 2Na_2O(s)$
    (d) $Fe(s) + 2HCl(aq)$
              $\rightarrow FeCl_2(aq) + H_2(g)$
    (e) $2Fe(s) + 3Cl_2(g) \rightarrow 2FeCl_3(s)$
3.   (a) $Na_2O(s) + H_2O(l) \rightarrow 2NaOH(aq)$
    (b) $2KClO_3(s) \rightarrow 2KCl(s) + 3O_2(g)$
    (c) $2H_2O_2(aq) \rightarrow 2H_2O(l) + O_2(g)$
    (d) $3Fe(s) + 2O_2(g) \rightarrow Fe_3O_4(s)$
    (e) $3Mg(s) + N_2(g) \rightarrow Mg_3N_2(s)$
    (f) $4NH_3(g) + 3O_2(g)$
              $\rightarrow 2N_2(g) + 6H_2O(g)$
    (g) $3Fe(s) + 4H_2O(g)$
              $\rightarrow Fe_3O_4(s) + 4H_2(g)$
    (h) $2H_2S(g) + 3O_2(g)$
              $\rightarrow 2H_2O(g) + 2SO_2(g)$
    (i) $2H_2S(g) + SO_2(g)$
              $\rightarrow 2H_2O(l) + 3S(s)$

Chapter 2

Problems on Relative Molecular Mass

64	40	101
84	278	95
148	99	161
98	63	246
136	685	142
106	74	123.5
159.5	162	249.5
400	286	278

Problems on Percentage Composition

Section 1

1.   Mg = 60%   O = 40%
2.   Ca = 40%   C = 12%
    O = 48%
3.   K = 39%   H = 1%
    C = 12%   O = 48%
4.   (a) N = 46.7%   O = 53.3%
    (b) H = 5%   F = 95%
    (c) Be = 36%   O = 64%
    (d) Li = 46.7%   O = 53.3%
5.   (a) C = 80%   H = 20%
    (b) Na = 57.5%   O = 40%
        H = 2.5%
    (c) S = 40%   O = 60%
    (d) C = 90%   H = 10%
6.   (a) C = 84%   H = 16%
    (b) Mg = 72%   N = 28%
    (c) Na = 15.3%   I = 84.7%
    (d) Ca = 20%   Br = 80%

Section 2

1.   (a) C = 85.7%   H = 14.3%
    (b) N = 35%   H = 5%
        O = 60%
    (c) Fe = 62.2%   O = 35.6%
        H = 2.2%
    (d) C = 26.7%   H = 2.2%
        O = 71.1%
2.   (a) Fe = 28%   S = 24%
        O = 48%
    (b) 40.5%   (c) 67.5%
    (d) 46.7%
3.   (a) C = 60%   H = 13%
        O = 27%
    (b) C = 40.0%   H = 6.7%
        O = 53.3%
    (c) C = 40.0%   H = 6.7%
        O = 53.3%
    (d) Al = 36%   S = 64%

Section 3

1.   34 000
2.   1.1 kg

Chapter 3

Problems on the Mole

Section 1

1. (a) 23 g (b) 24 g (c) 207 g
2. (a) 13.7 g (b) 5.2 g (c) 11.9 g
3. (a) 508 g (b) 216 g (c) 54 g
   (d) 402 g
4. (a) 27 g (b) 8 g (c) 6 g
   (d) 10 g (e) 5 g
5. (a) 2.0 (b) 0.05 (c) 0.75
   (d) 0.50 (e) 0.20 mol
6. (a) 44 g (b) 98 g (c) 36.5 g
   (d) 40 g
7. (a) 58.5 g (b) 28 g (c) 508 g
   (d) 265 g (e) 13.6 g
8. (a) 111 g; 123.5 g; 171 g; 85 g
   (b) 27.75 g; 30.87 g; 42.75 g;
       21.25 g

Section 2

1. (a) 26 g (b) 8 g (c) 4 g
   (d) 6 g (e) 4 g (f) 8 g
2. (a) 2.0 (b) 2.0 (c) 0.25
   (d) 0.10 (e) 0.25 mol
3. (a) 23 g (b) 7 g (c) 14 g
   (d) 8 g (e) 16 g (f) 32 g
4. (a) 1.0 (b) 2.0 (c) 0.33
   (d) 3.0 (e) 0.5 (f) 0.125 mol
5. (a) 2070 g (b) 10.6 g
   (c) 25.4 g (d) 20.0 g
   (e) 10.0 g (f) 40.0 g
   (g) 42.0 g (h) 13.0 g
   (i) 35.5 g (j) 2.00 g
6. (a) 1.00 (b) 0.25
   (c) 0.50 (d) 0.20
   (e) 0.20 (f) 3.0
   (g) 0.10 (h) 2.0
7. (a) 6×10^{23} (b) 6×10^{23}
   (c) 6×10^{22} (d) 3.6×10^{24}
   (e) 1.2×10^{24} (f) 6×10^{22}
   (g) 1.5×10^{22} (h) 1.2×10^{24}
8. (a) 65 g (b) 0.065 g
9. (a) 9.0 g (b) 0.027 g
10. (a) 12 g (b) 0.040 g
11. (a) 20.0 g (b) 12.0 g
    (c) 16.25 g (d) 115 g

Section 3

1. £1.25 × 10⁸
2. (a) 0.2 mol (b) 0.4 mol
   (c) 1.2 mol (d) 0.2 mol

3. 1.0×10^{23}
4. 55.5 mol
5. 6.3 mol
6. 3×10^{-23} g
7. 2.92 mol

Problems on Reacting Masses of Solids

Section 1

1. 40 g
2. 10 g
3. 44 g
4. 14.7 g
5. 32 g
6. 4 g
7. 50 g
8. (a) 63.5 g (b) 12.7 g
9. 4.4 g
10. 1 g
11. 12 g
12. 2.8 g

Section 2

1. 2.40 g
2. 23.2 g
3. 1 g
4. 22.3 g
5. 6.6 g
6. 8.0 g
7. 71 g
8. 27 g
9. 10.6 g
10. 170 g
11. C
12. D
13. B

Section 3

1. 1250 tonne
2. 0.05 g
3. 3.06 kg
4. 0.26 g
5. (a) $2O_2, 2H_2O$ (b) 2.25 kg
6. (a) $2Al(OH)_3, 3H_2SO_4, 3H_2O$
   (b) (i) 0.46 kg (ii) 0.86 kg
7. 25.0 kg
8. Loss of 83 p
9. (a) 72 g
10. (a) $3O_2 \rightarrow 2O_3$ (b) 64 g
11. 19 kg/year
12. (a) 1000 tonne (b) 1375 tonne
13. Yes, 1 mol C (12 g) combines with
    4 mol F⁻ (4 × 19 g)

14. 7.1 tonne
15. (a) 0.01 mol   (b) 0.02 mol
    (c) 2 mol
    (d) $Zn(s) + 2Ag^+(aq) \rightarrow Zn^{2+}(aq) + 2Ag(s)$
16. 127
17. (a) 0.56 g   (b) 8.0×10^{-2} mol
18. (a) 4.05 tonne   (b) 8.33 tonne
19. (a) (i) 1060 tonne (ii) 1030 tonne
    (b) natural limestone; manufactured
        ammonia
    (c) Ammonium sulphate is a fertiliser.

Chapter 4

Problems on Formulae

Section 1

1. Na_2O
2. Mg_3N_2
3. Fe_3O_4
4. $HgBr_2$
5. Al_2O_3
6. $BaCl_2 \cdot 2H_2O$
7. PbO_2
8. (a) C_7H_{16} (b) Mg_3N_2
   (c) Al_2S_3 (d) $CaBr_2$
   (e) Cr_2S_3

Section 2

1. (a) SO_2 (b) SO_3
   (c) NO (d) NO_2
   (e) CH_4 (f) CH_2
2. (a) P_2O_3 (b) NH_3
   (c) Pb_3O_4 (d) SiO_2
   (e) MnO_2 (f) N_2O_5
   (g) $CrCl_3$
3. $A = C_2F_4$ $B = C_4H_8O_2$
   $C = C_2H_6$ $D = C_6H_6$
   $E = C_3H_6$ $F = C_2H_6O_2$
   $G = C_2H_4Cl_2$ $H = C_6H_3N_3O_6$
4. (a) Na_2O (b) Pb_3O_4
   (c) NO_2 (d) Cu_2O
   (e) $FeCl_2$ (f) $FeCl_3$
5. (a) CO_2 (b) PbO_2
   (c) $CuCl_2$ (d) MgO
   (e) Mg_3N_2 (f) $AlBr_3$
6. (a) $MgSO_4 \cdot 7H_2O$
   (b) $CuSO_4 \cdot 5H_2O$
   (c) $Cr(NO_3)_3 \cdot 9H_2O$
7. (a) $MgSO_4$ (b) $N_2H_4O_3$
   (c) C_3H_8O (d) CH_2O

Section 3

1. $FeCl_3$
2. Br
3. 6
4. A
5. D
6. MO_2

Chapter 5

Problems on Reacting Volumes of Gases

Section 1

1. 24 dm³
2. 12 dm³
3. 2.4 dm³
4. 2.4 dm³
5. 250 cm³ O_2; 125 cm³ CO_2
6. 125 cm³ O_2

Section 2

1. 20.0 dm³ O_2; 20.0 dm³ CO_2
2. 25 g; 6.0 dm³
3. 3250 g; 1200 dm³
4. 480 cm³; 4.14 g
5. 120 cm³
6. 600 cm³
7. 0.41 g
8. 61.5 cm³
9. 120 dm³ O_2; 72.0 dm³ CO_2
10. 600 cm³; 1200 cm³

Section 3

1. (a) $2C_2H_6(g) + 7O_2(g) \rightarrow 4CO_2(g) + 6H_2O(g)$
   (b) 30 cm³   (c) 40%
2. C
3. C
4. CH_4
5. 20 cm³ ethane + 10 cm³ ethene
6. (a) 12.5 dm³   (b) 6.75 g
7. (a) 650 cm³   (b) 400 cm³
8. (a) 144 dm³   (b) 10.5 mol
   (c) 1260 dm³
9. (b) (i) 620 cm³   (ii) 330 cm³
   (c) 44, CO_2

Problems involving both Masses of Solids and Volumes of Gases

Section 4

1. £90 daily
2. (a) 0.30 mol   (b) 4.8 dm³
   (c) (i) 1.5 mol (ii) 1.0 mol
   (d) 2.5 g
   (e) 67 g
3. (a) KO_2
   (b) $4KO_2 + 2CO_2 \rightarrow 3O_2 + 2K_2CO_3$
   (c) 254 dm³
4. 3.5 g
5. (a) $2H_2O$ on RHS   (b) (i) 16.0 g (ii) 33.3 g
6. (a) $2H_2O$ on LHS   (b) 1.33 g
7. (a) 4.8 g   (b) 1.2 dm³
8. 180 cm³
9. 960 cm³
10. 12.0 dm³

Chapter 6

Problems on Concentration

1. (a) 0.0500 mol/dm³
   (b) 1.00 mol/dm³
   (c) 0.250 mol/dm³
   (d) 2.00 mol/dm³
   (e) 0.100 mol/dm³
   (f) 0.125 mol/dm³
   (g) 0.250 mol/dm³
   (h) 0.200 mol/dm³
2. (a) 0.250 mol   (b) 0.125 mol
   (c) 0.00500 mol   (d) 2.50 mol
   (e) 0.0500 mol   (f) 0.0250 mol
   (g) 0.370 mol   (h) 1.125 mol

Problems on Reacting Volumes of Solutions

Section 1

1. (a) True   (b) False
   (c) True   (d) False
   (e) True   (f) False
2. (a) True   (b) False
   (c) True   (d) False
   (e) True   (f) False
3. (a) False   (b) False
   (c) True   (d) True
   (e) True   (f) False

4. (a) True   (b) False
   (c) False   (d) False
   (e) True   (f) True

Section 2

1. 1.05 mol/dm³
2. 0.55 mol/dm³
3. 40 cm³
4. (a) 5.0×10^{-3} mol (b) 1.0×10^{-2} mol
   (c) 0.40 mol/dm³
5. 50 cm³ acid; 0.60 dm³ CO_2
6. (a) 2.0 mol/dm³   (b) 400 cm³
7. 33.3 cm³

Section 3

1. (a) 0.040 g/dm³   (b) 1.9×10^{-4} mol/dm³
2. 75%
3. (a) 1.1 mol/dm³   (b) 6.6%
4. 0.145 mol/dm³
5. 84%
6. No, concentration of $K^+ = 5.0 \times 10^{-3}$ mol/dm
7. Yes, concentration of $Li^+ = 2.0 \times 10^{-3}$ mol/dm
8. (a) 2.4 g   (b) 2.4 dm³
9. (b) 3600 dm³
10. (a) 1.5×10^{-6} g   (b) 1/30
11. (a) 0.050%   (b) 2.0×10^{-3} mol/dm³
12. 0.109 mol/dm³
13. (a) 1.20×10^{-2} mol (b) 1.20×10^{-2} mol
    (c) 1.20×10^{-2} mol
    (d) 0.276 g   (e) 9.2%
14. (a) 50 cm³   (b) 6.6 g
15. 19.2%
16. (a) 2.10×10^{-2} mol/dm³
    (b) 1.55 g/dm³
17. (a) 3.00×10^{-3} mol/l
    (b) 0.486 g/l

Chapter 7

Problems on Heat of Reaction

Section 1

1. 1380 kJ
2. 12.0 g
3. 85.5 g
4. 45 g
5. 4040 kJ
6. D

Section 2

1. (a) exothermic
    (b) (i) 55.6×10^3 kJ (ii) 49.6×10^3 kJ
2. (a) 12.5 l   (b) 230 kJ
    (c) 6.75 g
3. D
4. CH_4, 55.6 kJ/g: C_2H_2, 50 kJ/g
5. 13.3 kJ
6. H_2, 143 kJ/g: CH_4, 55.6 kJ/g; C, 32.5 kJ/g
7. (b) (i) -2010 kJ/mol (ii) -3950 kJ/mol
8. (b) 0.1 mol   (c) 2 mol/dm^3
    (d) 56 kJ   (e) 56 kJ
    (f) 112 kJ
9. (b) 30.0 cm^3 (c) 2.40 mol/dm^3

Problems on bond energies

1. (a) 2644 kJ/mol   (b) -3338 kJ/mol
    (c) $\Delta H = -694$ kJ/mol
2. -95 kJ/mol
3. -123 kJ/mol
4. -45 kJ/mol
5. -1070 kJ/mol

Chapter 8

Problems on Reaction Speeds

1. (a) 19 cm^3 (b) 30 s
    (c) 44 cm^3
2. A
3. C
4. C
5. (b) 0.55 g   (c) 10 min
    (d) 2.0 min
6. (a) $2H_2O_2(aq) \rightarrow O_2(g) + 2H_2O(l)$
    (c) 19.7 cm^3 (d) 4.3 min
7. (b) (i) 285 s   (ii) 65 s
    (c) increase   (d) increase
    (e) 20 s

Chapter 9

Problems on Solubility

1. 36.0 g/100 g
2. 27 g
3. 4 g of crystals form
4. (a) 50.0 g, 40.0 g, 33.3 g
    (d) 43.0 g/100 cm^3 water

5. 62.0 g (19.0 g KCl + 43.0 g KClO$_3$)
6. (a) NaCl   (b) 25 g
    (c) 30 g

Chapter 10

Problems on Radioactivity

Section 1

1. (a) 250 c.p.m.   (b) 125 c.p.m.
    (c) 62.5 c.p.m.
2. (a) 0.1 g   (b) 0.025 g
3. 9 s
4. 48 720 years
5. (a) $^{210}_{83}Bi$ (b) $^{206}_{82}Pb$
    (c) $^{24}_{12}Mg$ (d) $^{14}_{7}X$
    (e) $^{11}_{6}X$ (f) $^{27}_{14}Si + ^{1}_{0}Y$

Section 2

1. 11 400 years
2. (a) 2000 c.p.m.   (b) 250 c.p.m.
3. (b) 120 and 20 c.p.s.
    (c) (i) 33 min (ii) 54 min
    (d) 21 min   (e) 5 c.p.s.
    (f) 60 and 10 c.p.s.
    (g) 21 min
4. (a) 250 and 150 c.p.m.
    (b) (i) 115 days (ii) 250 days
    (c) 135 days
5. (b) 1 g

Section 3

1. (a) 56 years   (b) 6.25 g
    (c) 1.56 g   (d) 7
2. (a) 11p, 11e, 12n (b) 8p, 8e, 8n
    (c) 25p, 25e, 32n (d) 27p, 27e, 33n
    (e) 82p, 82e, 126n
3. 3.9×10^9 years
4. A 35 35 115, B 17 17 35, C 47 47 47,
    D 90 142 90, E 27 27 27
5. (a) $^{4}_{2}E$ (b) $^{90}_{37}E$
    (c) $^{146}_{62}E$ (d) $^{234}_{92}E$
6. (i) (a) $^{4}_{2}X$ (b) $^{2}_{1}X$
    (c) $^{0}_{-1}X$ (d) $^{1}_{0}X$
    (ii) (a) $^{4}_{2}He$ (b) $^{2}_{1}H$
    (c) $^{0}_{-1}e$ (d) $^{1}_{0}n$

Chapter 11

Problems on Electrolysis

Section 1

1. (a) 19.5 g K   (b) 10 g Ca
    (c) 51.8 g Pb   (d) 4.5 g Al
2. (a) 6 dm^3 H$_2$, 6 dm^3 Cl$_2$
    (b) 6 dm^3 H$_2$, 3 dm^3 O$_2$
    (c) 6 dm^3 H$_2$, 3 dm^3 O$_2$
3. 0.050 mol Cu
4. 120 cm^3
5. +3
6. D

Section 2

1. C
2. A
3. B
4. A
5. C
6. B

Section 3

1. 72 g Ca
2. +3
3. 204 hours
4. 27 minutes
5. 99.5 kg

List of Approximate Relative Atomic Masses

Element	Symbol	Atomic number	Relative atomic mass	Element	Symbol	Atomic number	Relative atomic mass
Aluminium	Al	13	27	Lithium	Li	3	7
Antimony	Sb	51	122	Magnesium	Mg	12	24
Argon	Ar	18	40	Manganese	Mn	25	55
Arsenic	As	33	75	Mercury	Hg	80	201
Barium	Ba	56	137	Neon	Ne	10	20
Beryllium	Be	4	9.0	Nickel	Ni	28	59
Boron	B	5	11	Nitrogen	N	7	14
Bromine	Br	35	80	Oxygen	O	8	16
Cadmium	Cd	48	112	Phosphorus	P	15	31
Caesium	Cs	55	133	Platinum	Pt	78	195
Calcium	Ca	20	40	Potassium	K	19	39
Carbon	C	6	12	Rubidium	Rb	37	85.5
Cerium	Ce	58	140	Selenium	Se	34	79
Chlorine	Cl	17	35.5	Silicon	Si	14	28
Chromium	Cr	24	52	Silver	Ag	47	108
Cobalt	Co	27	59	Sodium	Na	11	23
Copper	Cu	29	63.5	Strontium	Sr	38	87
Fluorine	F	9	19	Sulphur	S	16	32
Gold	Au	79	197	Tin	Sn	50	119
Helium	He	2	4	Titanium	Ti	22	48
Hydrogen	H	1	1	Tungsten	W	74	184
Iodine	I	53	127	Uranium	U	92	238
Iron	Fe	26	56	Vanadium	V	23	51
Krypton	Kr	36	84	Xenon	Xe	54	131
Lead	Pb	82	207	Zinc	Zn	30	65

Index

Acids 45
Alkalis 45
Atomic mass 6
Atomic Theory 33
Avogadro 12, 33
Avogadro constant 12
Avogadro's Hypothesis 33

Balancing equations 3
Bond energy 58

Catalyst 61
Cathode 80
Combining volumes of
        gases 33
Concentration 42
    and reaction speed 61
    of solutions 42
Coulomb 80

Electrolysis 80
Electric charge 80
Empirical formulae 26
Endothermic 53
Energy 53
Equations 2
    balancing 3
    from masses of
            reactants 19
    practice in 4
    from reacting volumes of
            gases 34
Exothermic 53

Formula unit 7
Formulae 1
    of electrovalent
            compounds 1
    empirical 26, 28
    molecular 28
    and percentage
            composition 8
    and relative molecular
            mass 7

Gases 33
    reacting volumes of 33
Gay-Lussac's Law 33
Graphs
    extent of reaction against
            time 61

radioactive decay 73
solubility 69

Half-life 74
Heat changes in chemical
        reactions 53
    of combustion 54
    of neutralisation 53
    of reaction 53, 54, 55

Ions 1
Isotopes 7, 74

Joule 53

Law
    Avogadro's 33
    Gay-Lussac's 33
Litre 33

Mass of product 16
Mass of reactant 16
Mass spectrometer 6
Masses of solids which
            react 12, 16, 19
Molar mass 13
Molar volume 33
Mole 12
    problems on 13
Molecular formula 28
    from empirical formula 28
    problems on 28

Neutralisation 45
Nuclear equations 76

Particle size 61
Percentage composition 8
    problems on 10
Problems on
    bond energies 59
    concentration 44
    electrolysis 84
    empirical formulae 28
    heat of reaction 55
    the mole 13
    molecular formulae 28
    percentage composition 10
    radioactivity 76
    reaction speeds 64
    reacting masses of
            solids 20

reacting volumes
    of gases 35
    of solutions 48
relative molecular mass 8
solubility 70

Radioactive decay 73
Radioactivity 73
    calculations on 74, 76
    problems on 76
Rates of chemical reactions 61
Ratio type of calculation 17,
        26
Reacting masses of solids 16
    equation from 19
    problems on 20
Reacting volumes of gases 33
    equation from 34
    problems on 35
Reacting volumes of
        solutions 42
    problems on 48
Reaction speeds 61
Relative atomic mass 6
    table of 5
Relative molecular mass 6
    calculation of 7
    problems on 8
Room temperature and
        pressure 33

Solubility 69
    calculation 69
    curve 69
    definition 69
    problems on 70
Solutions 69
    saturated 69
    standard 45
State symbols 2
Symbols 2

Titration 45

Valency 2
Volume units 33
Volumes
    of gases reacting 33
    of solutions reacting 42
    of gases in electrolysis 83

95